3-1-60

BIRD LIFE

Oxford University Press, Amen House, London E.C.4

GLASGOW NEW YORK TORONTO MELBOURNE WELLINGTON
BOMBAY CALCUTTA MADRAS KARACHI CAPE TOWN IBADAN

Geoffrey Cumberlege, Publisher to the University

TENGMALM'S OWL WITH ITS PREY, A BLUE TIT

Water-colour by Joseph Wolf

BIRD LIFE

BY

NIKO TINBERGEN

OXFORD UNIVERSITY PRESS
LONDON · GEOFFREY CUMBERLEGE
1954

CONTENTS

WHY DO WE WATCH BIRDS?

MANY of us are interested in birds. Some like to attract them to a feeding-tray in the garden. Others travel the whole weekend to see some very rare species on a remote island. Others again spend all their spare time cramped in a tiny hide just in order to see which species of caterpillar a particular bird feeds to its young. What urges us to do these things, and what is the use of them—if any? 1117432

People are interested in birds for different reasons. Birds are beautiful, and many of us enjoy looking at them. Birds are found in the open air, in beautiful scenery, and some of us become tired of concrete and pavement now and then, and enjoy being in the country. Birds are fellow creatures, and in a way are just as interesting as our fellow men.

But what is the use? Would it not be better to spend the time learning to repair a combustion engine, or learning to read the Classics?

To this I would say: if you like to play with your dog, and enjoy seeing him catch a ball or dash into the sea to retrieve a stick, don't you think you are better off than others who do not care about dogs at all? And birds are just as interesting as dogs, and as much pleasure is to be gained by watching a woodpecker chiselling out its nest hole or a lapwing luring a worm to the surface by causing miniature earthquakes with its feet.

But even if by 'use' you mean 'material advantage to mankind', there is much to be said in favour of bird-watching. Professional bird-watchers may be trying to find out why certain birds sometimes increase or decrease in numbers. When they know why, they may be able to tell us how to influence the numbers of animals that are of importance to us, either for good or for harm. An understanding of bird behaviour may even help us to understand our own instinctive behaviour. It is not surprising, therefore, that there are professional bird-watchers who are being paid for their work.

In this book I shall try to interest you in observing birds and in making discoveries of your own about how they live. I shall try to show you what kind of things you can see for yourself by using your own eyes, ears, and brain.

5

A DISCOVERY, AND
SOME QUESTIONS

Great tit

A BRIGHT winter morning. The air is crisp; the sun is still too low to have thawed the hoar frost on the fields. A short walk over the frozen common brings us to the edge of the wood. We need not go far now before we find our first birds: a flock of tits. Before we realize it they are all around us in the trees and shrubs, busily feeding. They hop along the boughs, hang in all kinds of positions, even upside down, inspect cracks in the bark, and look under the twigs. All the time we hear their calls, soft 'zee-zee-zee' notes. As they fly from bush to bush it looks as if each is going its own way; but, in fact, they are keeping together. They are not shy, and if we move with care and do not talk too loudly, they will not mind our presence.

All at once we hear some sharper and louder 'zee's'. Immediately all the tits dash into cover. Now something happens so fast that, before we realize what is happening, it is all over. A large, dark bird flashes across the scene, makes a few amazingly quick turns and, before we have time to have a good look at it, it is gone. It sails away and disappears into a dense patch of young pines.

What has happened? We heard a fluttering of wings; we believe we heard the impact when the large bird collided with one of the tits. When it flew away, something seemed to dangle

under it. This was a bird of prey, a sparrow hawk, and it has captured a tit. In nine out of ten cases this is all you see when such a thing happens—if, indeed, you notice it at all.

All we see after the event are a few downy feathers gently floating down from where the sparrow hawk caught its prey. The rest of the tits seem to have vanished; everything is silent.

Let us wait. Five minutes may go by, seven minutes. Silence. Then one of the tits calls softly. Then another one. There is some movement in the twigs; then all around us the tits reappear. They were only 'frozen', and had been staying motionless in the cover until the danger was past. Now they resume their feeding and calling.

This is what you usually see when a sparrow hawk collects its breakfast. Let us wait for another quarter of an hour, and then go to the pine plantation where the hawk disappeared. Ten to one the sparrow hawk has stayed there to eat its victim. It flies away at our approach, but it has left some traces behind. On and round a tree trunk we find a large patch of feathers: small downy feathers mostly; some grey, some cream-coloured, some bluish. Among them we find the quills of wings and tail. A bluish hue over them shows that the hawk picked a blue tit from the flock. With luck we may find its bill,

*Sparrow hawk
swooping down*

for that is usually left behind. All the rest has been neatly eaten.

This is a first-hand observation of two fundamental aspects of bird life. We saw tits and a sparrow hawk collecting their food, each in its own way. We saw, further, that tits are exposed to dangers : predators threaten and actually take their lives.

Feeding is part of the activities by which living things maintain themselves. Each animal 'earns a living' in some way or another. At the same time, there are adverse influences to which many animals succumb. Yet the species survive. That is, of course, because the deaths are, roughly speaking, made up for by births.

Here we have biology in a nutshell. How do living birds manage to maintain their kind, in spite of the heavy tolls taken by predators, by diseases, by starvation perhaps, and by other adversities? How do they select a fitting habitat, find their food, and breed? How do they protect themselves from predators? Why do they call and sing? Why are the species so different from one another—the skylark a dull grey, for example, and the mallard drake so gaudily coloured? What does an avocet do with its curiously curved-up bill? What are the mental capacities of birds?

By watching and seeing for yourself, you can make discoveries which will help you to understand how birds keep themselves alive and how they raise offspring which will take their place when they succumb—which inevitably they do sooner or later.

7

HOW BIRDS
MOVE ABOUT—1

BIRDS can move in a variety of ways. Their ability to fly is their most conspicuous asset, and their wings are their most striking characteristic. Some birds can also use their wings for swimming. Penguins are masters in this, as you can see in the London Zoo. Many waders can use their wings under water, particularly in an emergency. Birds further use their legs, for walking, hopping, climbing, or swimming. It is worth while to have a good look at these basic movements.

Let us look at bird flight first. Bird flight has aroused Man's admiration and envy since time immemorial; yet the way in which birds use their wings in flight has long remained obscure. It is not even fully understood yet. The movements of the wings in flight are difficult to see, but a good observer can acquire some understanding of it without experiments. Slow-motion cine-films, such as any amateur can make, of the gulls frequenting the London bridges are a great help.

When we compare a flying bird with an aeroplane, one difference is obvious. An aeroplane has separate 'organs' for propulsion (the propeller) and for lift (the wings). In birds, the wings serve both these functions. How the wings do this can be seen best by watching large birds. Let us first observe one that is gliding at leisure. Such a bird, when not in an updraught of air, is losing height all the time. It gets its speed from falling; but by spreading the wings and keeping their front edges a little lifted (so that the air flow hits the undersides) the fall is made very gradual. The shape of the wing in cross-section is beautifully streamlined. It is also slightly curved. This ensures a smooth flow of air across it, and engineers tell us that this gives a good speed and lift.

Black-headed gulls in flight

8

Sometimes gliding birds can be seen to stay up in the air for a long time, and even to gain height. This can usually be attributed to up-draughts: the birds are losing height in relation to the surrounding air, but the air is moving upward so fast that this compensates for the loss of height. Most birds are very clever in making use of such updraughts; on windy days the wind is forced upwards along hill-sides or above sloping roofs, and crows and gulls may ride these air currents for hours.

When a bird flies, it does something more than mere gliding. Large birds show 'flapping flight'—downstrokes alternate with upstrokes. In the downstroke, the bird gets lift by pressing the wings down on the air. In this, the parts far from the body near the wing-tips (the hands) are most effective, since they move over a greater vertical distance. The wings are fully stretched, offering a large surface area to the air. The downstroke also provides the bird with speed. This again is mainly the task of the 'hand'. The front edge is slightly lower than the hind edge, and thus the wing not only presses the air down, but back as well. This is essentially the same function as that of the plane's propeller. Of course, air resists being pressed down or back, and this resistance forces the bird up and forward.

In the upstroke, the front edge of the wing is raised, making the bird glide. This differs from normal gliding in that the downstroke has added speed to the 'fall'; also, the loss of height during the upstroke is compensated by the lift provided by the downstroke. The wing is also partially folded to reduce the resistance from the front during this non-propelling stage.

Small birds do not fall down during the up-stroke because, flapping their wings as rapidly as they do, the upstroke lasts so short a time. Many birds bring their wings up so rapidly that they press against the air with the wings' upper surface, and thus use the upstroke for forward propulsion as well. The humming birds are masters in this type of flight.

Cross-section of a bird's wing, showing streamlining by feathers

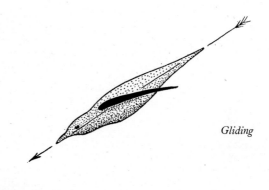

Gliding

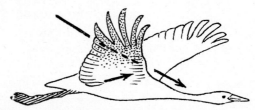

Flying crane, down-stroke; the hand 'propels'. The arrows indicate the cross-sections through the hand (broken line) and the arm (drawn line)

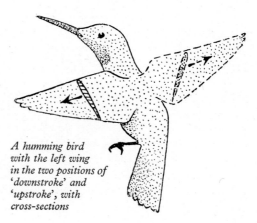

A humming bird with the left wing in the two positions of 'downstroke' and 'upstroke', with cross-sections

HOW BIRDS MOVE
ABOUT – 2

IT is fascinating to watch birds in flight, and to compare different kinds. Among the fastest are birds such as peregrine falcons, hobbies, and merlins—all birds which capture other birds in flight. They can reach tremendous speeds during flapping flight; in order to maintain this speed they may fold their wings almost entirely and fall nearly straight down. It is thrilling to see a hobby thus chase a swallow or a swift. Yet such birds need time to work themselves up to this high speed. Their start is slow, and their ability to make sharp turns is poor. Compare with that a pheasant, who starts like a rocket and gathers speed in a second, even in a steep ascent. Or see how agile a magpie is when pinching a cat's tail!

It is not difficult to see that these differences in type of flight go hand in hand with differences in the shape of the wings. In broad outline, these differences are of three kinds. Firstly, the total surface area of a wing is important. The larger the wing is in relation to the body of the bird, the more easily it will bear up the body; a buzzard can sail so well because of its long and broad wings. Secondly, the air at high speed will not flow smoothly over a very broad wing, and this reduces its speed; 'speed-birds', therefore, such as swifts and hobbies, have narrow wings. Thirdly, a long wing cannot be moved as fast as a short wing. Birds, therefore, which are experts in the art of starting quickly and turning suddenly, such as magpies and sparrow hawks, have short wings, and be-

cause for the same manœuvres the total wing area must be large, their wings are broad as well.

It is fascinating to study in detail the amazing agility birds can show when manœuvring in difficult circumstances. Two herring gulls were observed fighting in the air over a guillemot's egg; the gull which had the egg in its bill dropped it in the excitement of the fight, and the other gull turned instantly, flew down after it, caught it in the air, and then flew off triumphantly with the egg undamaged in its bill.

When fishing, a tern will hover in the air until it sees a fish, then plunge down into the water, and capture the fish in its bill. The correct steering of the plunge, simple though it may seem, is an achievement of the highest order.

Although birds have developed the art of flying to such a pitch of skill, they have not lost the ability to walk. Some birds have, indeed, very nearly lost this ability. Among the very best fliers are the swifts, and though they can crawl about (their walking does not deserve a better name), they rarely do it, and the main function of their feet is for hooking themselves on to a vertical wall. They even collect their nest material in mid-air. Very specialized swimmers have practically given up walking too; for instance, it is very unusual to see a grebe or a red-throated diver walk. On the other hand, there are birds that have specialized in walking and running. The small sanderling and wagtails, most plovers, and many fowl such as partridges have done this, without, however, losing their powers of flight. Completely flightless birds are either very large and power-

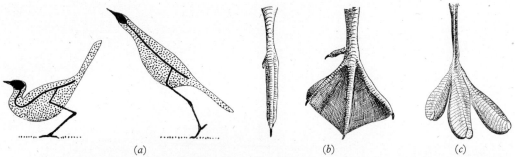

(a)   (b)   (c)

(a) The hop, the body withdrawn and stretched. (b) Left foot of duck, folded when moving forward through the water and spread when pushing against the water. (c) Left foot of grebe.

ful runners, such as ostriches, or they live in regions where there are no large predatory land mammals, like the kiwi of New Zealand. Penguins, too, can only survive because the antarctic does not harbour foxes and the like. In the arctic, the conditions are much the same except that there are foxes, and the guillemots and razorbills which live there have not lost their power of flight. In the past, flightless birds have lived on several oceanic islands where large predators were absent. They survived until the worst predator of all, Man, discovered them and killed them off. The curious, clumsy, and bulky dodo was one of these.

Many birds avoid solid ground altogether. Warblers, for instance, keep to the bushes and trees; bitterns, bearded tits, and others live almost entirely in the reeds. When a bittern comes to its nest in the marshes, it is amazing to see how its long toes take hold of a bundle of reeds and how, with long steps, it walks through the marsh forest, keeping well above the water.

Many birds hop. It is worth while having a close look at this primitive movement. Hopping is not only a matter of leg movements. Just before the hop, the whole body is contracted, and in the take-off every part is stretched. The body acts more or less in the way of a coiled spring. Once you have observed this, it is then obvious how many birds make this preparatory movement without actually hopping, especially when they feel inclined to move but cannot make up their minds, or do not really dare to.

Walking is a kind of dual hopping, or making a hop with each leg in turn. With each step, the body moves much as it does with each hop: it is first withdrawn and then stretched.

Birds swim either with their legs, as divers and diving duck do, or with their wings. The best wing-swimmers are the penguins, but many waders as well as auks and guillemots also swim with their wings. Wing-swimmers really fly under water. It is a curious kind of flight, though, because, as they are lighter than water, they do not have to provide lift to avoid sinking, as most animals do, but rather the reverse. When a guillemot or a diving duck returns to the surface, it does not need to fly up; it just stops flying, and at once it comes up as buoyantly as an air bubble.

The feet of each species are fitted to fulfil exactly the function required. Good walkers have long legs, climbers have long toes, swimmers have webbed feet of one kind or the other, a ptarmigan has a kind of snowshoe. Sometimes the foot is a compromise between two types: the foot of a goose, for example, though well adapted to swimming, is more suitable for walking than that of a grebe.

Magpie and cat

FEATHERS

AND

PLUMAGE

Nightjar with chick: flashlight photograph

YOU have probably noticed how fluffy birds become during cold weather. This is because the air among the feathers acts as an insulating coat, preventing the loss of valuable body heat. The strong quill feathers of wings and tail enable the bird to fly.

It is worth while inspecting the feathers of any dead bird you may find, or looking at the feathers lost by birds in the field. Almost the whole of a bird's body is covered with small feathers. Feathers of a different type are found on the wings and tail. The largest part of the wing is equivalent to a human hand; it bears the long, strong feathers which are called primaries. The arm, which is usually shorter than the hand (if we include the primaries), bears the secondaries. The tail usually has twelve strong tail-feathers. These long and strong feathers of both wing and tail are covered at their base by a coat of smaller ones, the upper- and under-wing coverts, and the upper- and under-tail coverts. Bird handbooks, such as those mentioned on p. 62, will give the system of names applied to the various parts of the body and the plumage.

Each feather has a shaft with two vanes. Each vane is made up of innumerable parallel bristle-like structures, the barbs. Under a lens it is possible to see how each barb has a row of tiny hooks which seize corresponding hooks on the next barb. When hooked together they support each other. Each single feather is a complicated structure and made of excellent material: it is flexible and yet very strong, and above all it is elastic. This strength and elasticity is the reason for the remarkably long life of the downy feathers in a camping quilt or feather bed which has to bear the full weight of a sleeping person night after night.

Yet even feathers wear. All birds, therefore, spend much time keeping their plumage in order. By preening they rub the vane and thus make the bristles hook into each other when they have come apart. In spite of this care, feathers have to be renewed at intervals. They fall out, and new feathers grow in their place. This moult occurs once or twice a year, or even more often in some species. The shedding of quill feathers is done in various ways, each nicely adapted to the needs of the particular

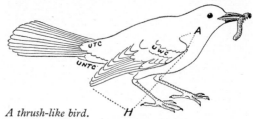

A thrush-like bird.
A = arm; H = hand; UTC = upper tail coverts;
UNTC = under tail coverts; UWC = upper wing
coverts

12

species. The feathers used for flight rarely drop out all at once; this occurs only in birds which can afford to lose their power of flight for a while—birds of wide muddy plains or of marshes, such as ducks and geese. Shelduck and some geese even migrate over long distances before the moult to reach safe places, free from predators, in which to spend that helpless period. Other ducks become very shy and retire to dense reeds during the moult.

Feathers are dead structures formed by the skin, like human hairs. Building them up requires much food; also, the moult impairs flight. Moulting birds, therefore, lead a very subdued life during the moult to avoid wasting energy or catching the eye of hawks. That is why during the late summer the woods seem relatively dull and empty of birds. Nature has timed the moult so that it comes after the young have been reared and before autumn migration sets in.

The plumage has still another important function: it is responsible for the bird's colour. Many birds are camouflaged for protection against their enemies. They carry their camouflage coloration on those parts of their bodies that are normally exposed to sight—not, for instance, under the wings or on the underside of the body. Few things in nature are more beautiful than the plumage of an owl or of a nightjar, which, with its marvellous pattern of white, brown, and black dots and lines, imitates the bark of trees. The picture of a nightjar, though one of the finest in existence, gives only a vague impression of the reality.

Ducks and geese grow a special kind of down

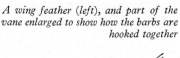

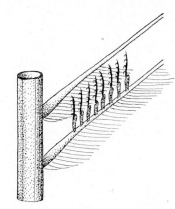

A wing feather (left), and part of the vane enlarged to show how the barbs are hooked together

under the plumage on their breasts. The incubating female plucks this and arranges it round her eggs to cover them when she leaves the nest. This down often matches the environment and so provides a camouflaged nest.

The amazing colourful patterns of the mating plumage of some birds are designed to attract notice. Bright patches, bands, shields, and so on, are made up of many feathers. If you examine the feathers of a mallard drake, from its glossy green head and white collar to its brown breast, you will see how the feathers make the pattern. On the head there are completely green feathers, then green feathers with white tips, then pure white feathers, then white ones with brown tips, and finally brown breast-feathers. As feathers get worn first at the tips, many birds look rather shabby in the late summer just before their moult.

Plumages, feathers, moult, and everything that is related to them form a fascinating field of study. An attractive detective job for the summer is to collect the feathers from week to week from a place where flocks of birds gather. From the weekly collections it should be possible to reconstruct the order in which the various feathers moult, and this may suggest some interesting facts about how the birds live.

Wing of goose. A = arm; H = hand: primaries have both vanes shaded, secondaries have one vane shaded

Male wheatear with food at nest entrance

ON EYESIGHT AND HEARING

ONCE I watched a pair of wheatears collecting food for their young. I saw them hop through the short grass, searching for prey. Every few minutes one of them had gathered a beakful of insects, among them fat caterpillars, which it brought to the young, who were in the nest in a rabbit warren. I was anxious to try to compete with them, and find out how abundant food was. But try as I could, I did not find anything worth while! Yet I prided myself on being a pretty good observer, able to find many kinds of insects where others failed. But these wheatears had sense organs which were clearly much better than mine.

Relatively little is known about the sense organs of birds. We do know, however, that they rely mainly on vision and on hearing, and that their powers of smell are poorly developed; otherwise they would not remain so undisturbed by the presence of a man well hidden from sight. In that respect they are very different from mammals, which easily detect observers by smell, however well they may be hidden.

Very few birds can smell. There is still some uncertainty about the sense of smell of duck, and there is evidence that vultures can smell. Most probably the curious, flightless kiwi of New Zealand has a well-developed sense of smell. But most birds depend mainly on their eyes and ears.

Evidence of good hearing is easy to get. Birds react to each others' calls. You can often see this in birds that breed in holes, who often react to the young even though they cannot see them. Incubating gulls often doze on the nest, but wake up when they hear their own mate. Owls are probably champions of hearing, and are worth a close study in that respect.

The eyesight of most birds is excellent. They can look at things with both eyes, just as we do.

Black-headed gull looking up with one eye

But often they look at an object with one eye, tilting their head when they do so. By watching this movement in song-birds, I have often discovered the presence of birds of prey circling very high up in the sky. On one occasion I saw a thrush watching with alarm something in the sky. I had considerable difficulty in discovering anything, and only with my powerful field-glasses was I able to recognize that it was a buzzard. Yet the thrush had discovered it with the naked eye. When flocks of waders are feeding along the seashore in winter, they will discover an approaching peregrine or merlin from an amazingly great distance.

Sometimes it is possible to compare the sharpness of a bird's sight with that of one's own by comparing the distance at which they see an object with the distance at which one can see it oneself. I have often measured carefully the distance from which a hobby saw a dragonfly; it varied from about 100 to well over 200 yards. I myself could not see these dragonflies from more than about 90 yards away. Such observations have rarely been done, yet they are not very difficult to make, and since the eyes of birds are the best eyes found in the animal kingdom, precise figures of their capacities are of more than ordinary interest.

Other proof of the good eyesight of birds is afforded by the many cases in which birds have been shown to recognize each other individually. I have often seen a herring gull, for example, recognize its mate among dozens of others from a distance of more than 25 yards, even when the mate did not call; and it is known that young jackdaws can tell from a considerable distance whether or not their parents are carrying food.

There is a simple experiment to find out whether a bird reacts to something by eyesight or not. Many birds are very aggressive in spring. When you put up a mirror near the favourite perch of such a bird, you will often see that it attacks its own image in the mirror. That can mean only that it ordinarily recognizes its adversary by sight.

The sense of taste is well developed in many birds. Most of them will reject strongly salted food, for instance. They also have a sense of touch. Perhaps the most sensitive organs of touch are found in the bills of snipe. These birds find much of their food with their bills deep down in the mud, and they seem able to feel with their bill-tips what is suitable for food.

Young hobby looking at camera with both eyes

HOW BIRDS GET THEIR FOOD

Common tern plunge-diving

THE more I have watched birds, the more I realize how extremely varied are the methods by which birds find their food, and how very clever many of these methods are. The way they discover food, the way they distinguish between various types of food, the way they prepare it, the specialized organs they use— each of these aspects is very interesting. Each species has different methods for finding and dealing with the particular food it needs. The limitations of each species—what it cannot do as well as what it can—are equally interesting.

Most birds, no doubt, look for their food with their eyes. But the animals they prey upon often live concealed. How does a thrush discover an earthworm? How does a woodpecker find insect larvae under the bark? Can an owl see mice in the night? These are a few of the many things well worth finding out.

All birds select their food carefully. Chickens in the farmyard, for example, pick up grains, crumbs, and an occasional insect, rejecting the rest. None but the very young and inexperienced take a wasp, though they may take a fly. If you follow a chick feeding from the moment it hatches, you will see that it is not so selective at first, but it gradually learns to leave alone the inedible or the distasteful objects. But many birds instinctively know without experience what to eat and what not. A common tern never picks up grains, which are unsuitable food for tern; it dives for fish.

We do not know much about what various birds eat and how they find, get, and prepare their food. This is an interesting subject which still needs much accurate observation.

Once the bird sees and recognizes the food it wants, it may still often have difficulty in getting it. That is especially true of the hunters. Many birds can catch insects in flight; the fly-catchers, as their name indicates, are masters at doing this. They sit on a look-out post until they see an insect, then they dart into the air, make one or two sharp turns, catch their prey, and return to their post. A sparrow often tries to do the same thing, but its comparatively clumsy efforts are seldom successful. Swallows, swifts, and nightjars, on the other hand, do all their searching and hunting on the wing.

Most fascinating of all are the bird-hunting birds of prey, for both the hunter and the hunted perform absolutely breath-taking evolutions during the chase, and the outcome is never certain. Where there are large flocks of waders, of song-birds, or of teal, it is often possible to see a peregrine falcon, or the smaller merlin, on the chase. A peregrine may approach low over the mudflats, accelerating with formidable wing beats to a terrific speed, making straight for a distant bird flock. With glasses you can watch the chase. Long before the falcon reaches the

Avocet feeding: an attempt to indicate the mowing movements of the head

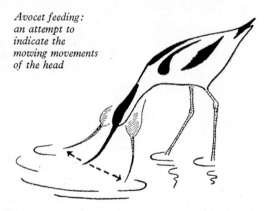

birds, they have seen it and go up, flying in a very dense formation and manœuvring left and right in quick turns. It takes the peregrine only a few seconds to reach the flock, and then it makes a wide turn and swoops past it—rarely through it. The falcon then rises steeply into the air, turns round, and again swoops down. If one of the small birds in the meantime has lost contact with the flock—as in the intense agitation one or two often do, failing to perform a quick turn in time—the falcon is after it like lightning, and often gets it. It then sails away, the hapless victim dangling from its talons, and settles somewhere on a hummock to kill, pluck, and devour it.

A sparrow hawk or a goshawk uses very different methods. Both hunt by flying low over trees and bushes, dashing down into open spaces where they hope to surprise a bird or a flock. Surprise is their main tactic; they cannot fly as fast as the peregrine. Before the surprised jay or sparrow can gain speed, the hawk is upon it. If it does not catch its prey first time, it brakes and turns with great agility, often following its quarry right into cover, turning and twisting and even crashing right through the bushes.

Another type of very specialized hunting is practised by fishing birds. Some, like the cormorant, swim under water and with great skill hunt the fleeing fish. Others, such as terns and the kingfisher, plunge-dive. This may not need so much agility under water, but the aiming of the dive must be extremely difficult. The gannet applies a combination of the two methods.

The preparation of the food often involves quite complicated behaviour, and the organs used, in particular the bills, are well adapted to their function. If you watch a duck dabbling in the duckweed at close quarters, you will see how rapidly it manages to sieve the water through its bill. An avocet has a curiously up-curved bill. This is used when the bird feeds in shallow water, 'mowing' the bill just under the surface so that the tip is just about horizontal.

Head of a mallard, showing bill 'sieve'

Oystercatchers have a very clever method of opening mussels. When at rest in shallow water, a mussel has its valves slightly opened. The oystercatcher thrusts its bill, flattened like a knife, into the slit, and then turns the bill round its long axis. Since most mussels are firmly attached to the ground, and cannot turn round, this pivoting movement forces the two halves of the shell apart, so that the bird can get at the animal inside. A gull takes the shellfish in its bill, flies up, and then drops the shell from a height of ten or fifteen yards, so that when it hits hard ground it crushes. Thrushes, as we have often seen, smash snail shells by taking them in their beaks and hitting them on a stone until the shell cracks. Hawfinches, who want to eat the kernels of the yew berries on which they often feed, crack the stones with their remarkable strong beaks.

Shrikes, which unlike most birds catch and eat wasps, have a special way of taking the sting out before they eat them. I have seen my captive song-thrushes take another precaution against being stung: they give the wasp a formidable peck and immediately jump back before the wasp can sting. They repeat this several times until the wasp is dead. It is known that fly-catchers also eat wasps, but I do not know whether they have any way of getting rid of the sting.

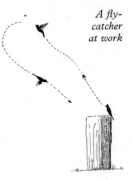

A fly-catcher at work

HOW BIRDS PROTECT
THEMSELVES FROM PREDATORS

BIRDS, naturally, use their wings in escaping from predators. In particular, their powers of flight are useful in avoiding most predatory mammals, for they have only to fly up in a tree to be completely out of reach. And that is what they do. Most birds, even those which find their food on the ground, are reluctant to come to the ground. Once you are aware of that, you can understand many aspects of bird behaviour. Birds with pinioned or otherwise damaged wings are much less willing to come down than normal ones. Young birds have to acquire a high level of perfection of their flying abilities before they venture to roost on the ground. I have often watched young hobbies from the day they left the nest till their departure six weeks later. During the first few weeks they spend their whole day in the trees, and although they fly a great deal, and are very clumsy at alighting on a tree, they never come down to the ground. Only when they are accomplished fliers do they roost on the ground occasionally, but then only on flat ground where there is a clear view all round. The first reaction of caged song-birds, even at the slightest disturbance, is to fly upwards. That is why a cage or an aviary can have quite large doors provided they are in the lower half of the cage, for as soon as the door is opened, even tame birds will usually fly up on to one of the perches.

But birds have their enemies in the air as well, some of them highly skilled fliers, and various birds have developed different defences against them. Good fliers, such as pigeons, often save themselves by simply out-flying the enemy, and by dodging a predator such as a peregrine falcon when it strikes. Other species, among them even excellent fliers such as swallows, dash into cover when they get the chance. As we described on page 6, that is what the tits did when attacked by the sparrow hawk. Duck plunge or even fly down into the water and dive. Even land birds may resort to the water in such cases. Godwits have been observed to throw themselves flat on to the water, to rise again only after the peregrine has left. Crows may do that also.

A very nice way of hiding in cover is practised by the great spotted woodpecker, and possibly by related species as well. When it is surprised by a sparrow hawk while feeding on a strong limb of a tree, it immediately slides down to the underside of the branch and stays there, 'frozen', until the danger is over. 'Freezing', of course, is resorted to by many birds, and is most

Great spotted woodpecker hiding under branch as a reaction to a sparrow hawk (top left)

effective when done by birds with good camouflage colouring, such as partridges and larks.

Birds living in flocks not only react individually when they see a bird of prey, but they warn each other. It is great fun, and very instructive as well, to try to fool such birds by imitating the alarm call. The long-drawn 'huu-uui' of warblers, for instance, can easily be imitated, and once you have mastered the call, you can make many opportunities of studying the reactions of the warblers to danger.

If you have ever watched domestic fowl on free range you may have noticed that they have two different alarm calls. A long-drawn 'raaaa' is used when a bird of prey appears suddenly in the sky; in fact it is uttered whenever a largish bird such as a pigeon or a jackdaw flies over. The 'koo—koko-kokokoKOOOOO-ko!' (the same call as that uttered by a hen just after having laid an egg) is the alarm for a ground predator or for a sitting hawk—that is, for a predator that is not likely to take them by surprise. The reactions of the other hens to the calls are different: the first call makes them all look up, and in extreme cases crouch; the other call evokes a tendency to fly up on to a branch. Many other birds have a similar set of two calls, one used as a mild warning, the other as a sign of sudden danger.

The advantages of social life are not confined to these mutual warning calls alone, useful as they are. Many social birds actually attack the predator in mass, and harass it to such an extent that hunting becomes wellnigh impossible. You may have watched house sparrows when they have seen a cat in the garden: they cluster above it in a bush and by their continuous 'chèw-chèw-chèw!' arouse the whole bird neighbourhood. Starlings, wagtails, and many other social song-birds often react to a passing sparrow hawk by climbing above it in the air, and following it wherever it goes. Usually the hawk gives up hunting and flies off to try its luck elsewhere.

Once I observed a male lapwing protect his

Wagtails 'mobbing' a sparrow hawk

fully-fledged but inexperienced family from a cat by a most remarkable type of behaviour. The cat was walking stealthily in a meadow, and the young lapwings, aroused by it, were flying round, calling the alarm-call 'pee-wit, pee-wit'. Every now and then one would alight as near as five or ten yards from the cat, and immediately the greatly excited father would dash down on it and chase it away. When we remember how rigidly birds usually follow their relatively simple instinctive modes of behaviour, we realize how extraordinary this behaviour of the lapwing was.

Another type of behaviour against predators is the 'distraction display' which so many bird parents perform when their brood is in danger. They flutter down to the ground, and behave as if they are wounded, or they imitate the running away of a vole, at the same time moving and spreading tail and wings, which makes them very conspicuous. Predators are often fooled by this and start to follow the displaying bird, which invariably lures them away from the brood. As soon as the enemy is sufficiently far away from the brood, the bird parent makes an unexpected recovery. It is not at all difficult to see these things happen, because most birds are just as afraid of us as they are of a stoat or a fox. With perseverance you may one day be lucky enough to see a whitethroat or some such bird play this trick on, say, a stoat, and then you can see for yourself whether it works or not.

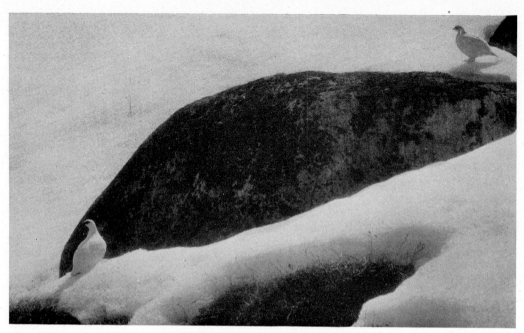

Ptarmigans in their spring habitat in Greenland

THE HABITATS OF BIRDS

DIFFERENT birds live in different types of localities, in different habitats. We go to the sea cliffs when we want to see guillemots, and not to sandy heaths. We go to sandy coast or to skerries for terns. Jays live in the woods, but skylarks in open grassy plains, and grebes on lakes.

Apart from these large differences there are more subtle ones. Grebes live on one kind of lake, bearded tits by another. Jays and long-eared owls live in different types of wood. One can safely say that no two species of British birds live in exactly the same habitat. Lapwing and redshank both live in marshy meadows, but while the redshank is usually found nesting in high grass, a lapwing usually avoids it, choosing places where the vegetation is short. It is worth while to try to describe the type of habitat typical of each bird species, and to find out how the bird's mode of life fits this habitat exactly, and what makes the bird live in one place, and not in another. The lapwing, for instance, does not lift its feet when it walks, nor does it fold the toes back, and therefore it has some difficulty in walking among high grasses. The redshank, on the other hand, avoids getting grass caught between its toes by deftly lifting its feet at each step and folding its toes back. The straight flight of a starling makes it unfit to live among thick foliage and shrubbery, and therefore it rarely ventures into dense forest. A jay, on the other hand, is a master in quick turning and in steep ascents and descents, and is quite at home in dense shrubbery.

Many birds live in one habitat in the breeding season and another in winter. Most petrels are not found on or even near land outside the breeding season, unless they are ill. Many duck live along the seashore in winter but breed on freshwater lakes.

We might ask what directs each species to its own habitat. Is their choice haphazard, those who happen to go to the wrong places getting killed, just as many plant seeds are thrown out and fall into the right soil or perish? A little observation shows that this is not so: birds select their habitat. But how can they know which habitat is best for them? Some birds may learn where to settle because their parents guide them at first; but a young heron, for instance, is independent as soon as it leaves its nest in the tree-tops, and it makes straight for the water and finds its own right food. So its knowledge of the kind of place where it can find food must be inborn.

Sometimes a bird species changes its range. This always provides a good opportunity for the study of the selection of habitat. The fulmar, in recent years, has been observed to spread south along the British coast. On the European continent the wild canary, the missel thrush, the black woodpecker, and other species have recently settled in countries where they did not exist half a century ago. Often we do not know whether these changes are due to a change in the bird's preference for a special habitat or whether the land, by some subtle change, has

become suited to them. A change of the latter type has been shown to be the cause of the arctic Bewick's swans wintering in increasing areas of the Zuiderzee in Holland. After the Zuiderzee, in 1932, was shut off from the North Sea by a dike, its water became fresh in the course of a few years. Gradually thousands of swans, which had always wintered round the mouth of the river Ijssel, spread out along most of the Zuiderzee coast. An investigation showed that they lived on the roots of a water weed which, as the water lost its salinity, spread from the Ijssel mouth along the greater part of the coast, and the swans followed the weed. A similar extension of the food supply is probably the cause of the fulmar's spread. In the last half-century the expansion of the fisheries has provided the fulmars with abundant supplies of offal in regions where, earlier, food had been too scarce for them to live.

Areas where man is changing the face of the country, for instance, by covering heathland with pine plantations, afford unique opportunities of following the changes in the bird population as the forest grows up. By watching the birds' habits, you may understand why these changes occur.

Habitat of pied flycatcher in the Forest of Dean

SONG

Male house sparrow singing on his nest-box

THE song of many birds seems beautiful to us. That is why it is called song, for it reminds us of human song. We do not know whether birds themselves consider their song beautiful, although we like to believe that they do. What birds feel we will never know, because they have no means of telling us. But we do know other things about bird song.

If we watch a male song-bird, such as a nightingale or a chiffchaff, early in the morning in early spring, just after it has arrived from its winter quarters, we shall notice that it is alone and has not yet got a mate. It spends most of its time singing, making perhaps short breaks for foraging for food, but almost immediately returning to its perch to sing again. If we watch closely we will see that while it sings it looks continually round in all directions. It is clearly very much on the alert.

If we continue to watch this bird from day to day we shall notice that it is singing every morning, usually from the same few perches. As the days go on, the vigour of its song increases. Suddenly, one day, there is no singing bird. It has not left, however; a close scrutiny of the bushes will soon show that it is still there. But since our last visit a female has arrived, and our male is silent because it has mated. The pair keeps close together, now and then the male courting or pursuing the female; but it does not sing. The sudden change in its behaviour is striking.

This behaviour is not accidental; it is the rule in many species. The newly arrived male sings persistently in order to attract a female. But we might well ask why it should stop singing when the song has served its purpose; why should not the male continue to sing just for pleasure even after the female has arrived? The reason is that so many natural events are determined by their

usefulness. Song makes the male conspicuous. But it makes it conspicuous not only to the female but also to predators, who find it much more difficult to locate a silent bird than one which advertises its presence by singing. Song is uttered, therefore, in many species at least, only when it is necessary. It is very useful for the purpose of bringing male and female together, but as soon as this is accomplished, it is merely dangerous; our male would run the risk of being killed by a cat or a sparrow hawk before it had the chance of rearing young.

There are birds which for reasons unknown to us can afford to sing much more than is strictly necessary. Thus blackbirds sing a great deal on summer evenings when all known functions of its song have been fulfilled. Their song at these times is even richer and more varied than in the mating season, and we cannot help believing that these birds sing just for the fun of it. And for some reason they can afford to take the risk.

How, then, do males of species that do not sing manage to attract females? That depends entirely on the species. Many species, such as gulls and terns, live in flocks, and return year after year to the same colony sites. There they can see each other, and need not guide solitary females by song. Other species, although they do not 'sing' as we mean it, do make specific loud noises which have exactly the same function as song. We are not accustomed to call these noises 'song', simply because they are not so beautiful nor so persistent as, say, the song of a nightingale. A male grey heron gives a loud, raucous cry every half minute or so as long as it is unmated, and this cry attracts the female herons. The rattling of the male nightjar, though rarely called 'song', serves the same purpose of attracting the females. The great spotted woodpecker 'drums', and probably attracts females by this 'instrumental music'. A friend of mine once made a little instrument out of an old alarm clock, which imitated the drumming very well. If you managed to make a similar instrument, and if you played it just as persistently as a male woodpecker drums, morning after morning, you could perhaps attract female woodpeckers. Also, I think if you took one of Ludwig Koch's fine gramophone records of bird songs, and played it in the suitable habitat in spring, you would get surprising results.

You would then find that song has a second function as well: it signals the presence of males to other males. By imitating the woodpecker's drumming near an occupied territory my friend could make the owner of the territory fly to its favourite drumming tree and reply. You can do a similar thing to many male birds. Most bird songs are not very easy to imitate, but a golden oriole, for instance, is easily fooled by even a crude imitation of its melodious call. If you play one of Ludwig Koch's records near the place where a male of the species is living, it will reply at once and, further, it will come to you. If you are well concealed, it may come very close, and then you may see how it looks around, as if searching for something. You can extend this little experiment by taking some mounted birds along with the gramophone. When you play a chaffinch record, the chances are that you attract a male chaffinch. It you put a mounted

male chaffinch and, say, a mounted robin and a greenfinch near the gramophone, the male will attack the stuffed chaffinch but ignore the others. This shows what the bird was looking for when it was attracted by the song. And it shows how song and visual characteristics work in nature: a male bird goes to where it hears a rival singing, then looks for it and attacks it.

This, however, is done only by birds which have settled on a chosen spot. Other males that are still wandering react quite differently to their species' song. They get scared, and withdraw when they hear a rival.

We see, therefore, that song serves more than one purpose. It attracts females and thus brings the sexes together for mating and breeding. But it keeps the males apart, forcing each to go and find a place of its own, and helping each, once settled, to locate and drive off intruders. Song thus serves as a kind of signal. Usefulness and beauty go together, as is so often the case in nature.

Male great spotted woodpecker drumming

FIGHTING

Male chaffinches fighting

SOME hours of an early morning in April spent watching the ways of the chaffinches, or robins, or other common song-birds in a neighbourhood, will show that the males are all in a very aggressive temper. They chase each other, posture at each other, and even occasionally indulge in a 'man-to-man' fight. Chaffinches may hover in front of each other, trying to seize each other with their feet, or giving each other fierce pecks with their bills. If they come to grips, they may fall on the ground and be so absorbed in their struggle that you can almost touch them.

This spring aggressiveness is typical of most cock birds. Each species has its own fighting technique: waterhens strike with their long-toed feet; pigeons give violent wing blows; gulls use their wings and their bills.

It is worth while to follow two such fighting males for some time. Usually it is possible to distinguish between the two by slight differences in size, in plumage, in manners, in voice. Each of them keeps to its own piece of ground, or 'territory', the fights taking place somewhere in the border zone between the two territories. When *B* ventures too far into *A*'s territory, *A* attacks and *B* withdraws. *B* is no coward or weakling, however, for if *A* intrudes into *B*'s territory, then *B* attacks and *A* retreats. The outcome of the fight depends almost entirely on the 'morale' of the combatants, and the 'morale' of a bird is highest when it is on its territory.

When you follow the events in a certain area in the course of spring, you will see that there are only a few territory-owners at the beginning, who share the whole area between them, but that now and then new-comers arrive, and try to settle on already occupied ground. Early comers may succeed, if only after heavy fighting, but later in the season it becomes increasingly difficult to settle, and many later claimants are fought off. Although we are now getting to know a great deal about these things, we do not yet know enough; it is not only fascinating but also of scientific importance to follow very accurately the way in which birds take possession of such an area. The best plan is to begin by drawing a map and marking where the males are singing, where they drive others off, and where they are driven off themselves. Then we can note down to which other birds they react and to which they do not; what things they do during the day; when the females arrive and how the males react to them, and so on and so on. All this can make a very interesting story. Apart from the things which we set out to observe, many other quite unexpected things may happen. A sparrow hawk may chase one of the birds we are observing; squirrels may come and forage near by; a stoat may appear on a hunting trip, and if so, it may be mobbed by the birds—though if a hare or a rabbit should appear, it will not be mobbed. All such things may happen all around us if we sit quietly in our observation hide-out and watch intently.

Threatening male black-headed gull

But let us return to our fighting birds. Actual fights are rare, but mutual threat is frequent. A study of how birds threaten each other is very rewarding. Usually a territory owner has only to adopt a threat posture to drive an intruder off. That is why we are justified in calling such postures 'threat'.

A threatening bird often turns its main weapon—the bill—towards its opponent. In addition, it may show off by fluffing its plumage, or by displaying brightly coloured parts. Thus a robin turns its red breast towards an opponent. Chaffinches display the white 'epaulets'. Great tits point their bills up, and slowly turn their heads left and right, thus displaying their bright black-and-white head pattern. Black-headed gulls adopt the 'forward' posture, showing off their bills and their brown faces and lifting the

Threatening male chaffinch, displaying 'epaulets'

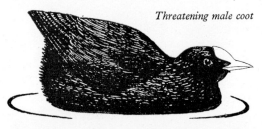

Threatening male coot

wings so that they can give a wing blow if needed. Coots lower their heads, showing their white frontal plates at their best. Even the tiny goldcrest displays the only gaudy feature it has got: it raises its orange crest. When watching such displays you get a glimpse of the function of these brightly coloured structures.

What is the significance of all this fighting? It is becoming more and more clear that it is of great advantage for each species to space itself out. Fighting and threat prevent birds of one species from nesting too close together. This is, for various reasons, likely to be harmful to birds when they are breeding. It is probable that nesting too close together would in unfavourable circumstances exhaust the local food supply and thus starve the young. Kestrels, jackdaws, starlings, and many other birds nesting in holes concentrate their defence round the holes. Since

good holes are often scarce, and since two families would certainly harm each other if crowded into one hole, the main function of fighting in these birds is probably to force all to find holes for themselves. In species such as lapwings and gulls, spacing out seems to reduce the risks to the broods of being eaten by predators; if broods were close together a predator might specialize on them since they are easy to find; but if they are so much spaced out that they are difficult for a predator to find, they may prove to be so unprofitable a source of food that the predator looks elsewhere.

Threatening male robin

COURTSHIP

IN spring, male birds can often be seen performing a variety of curious antics in front of females. A male turkey droops his wings, spreads his beautiful tail, makes his wattles swell, and utters a deep-sounding 'whrooooommmmmm'. A male lapwing sits down in a 'scrape' (the beginning of its nest), lifts its tail, and turns its beautiful chestnut under-tail coverts towards the female. Many male birds, among them jays and other song-birds, gulls, and terns, present food to the female. When we see such things, we say that the males are courting the females.

Male black-headed gulls—which can be distinguished from females by their slightly heavier build and by their aggressiveness—take up territories like many song-birds, and here they are visited by females. A male who has settled in a territory utters the 'long call' at each bird, male or female, that passes overhead, and if a female responds to this and alights, the male suddenly adopts the 'forward posture'. At first sight this use of the long call and the forward posture in front of a female is surprising, for both are threat postures. Yet this seems to be the rule in many birds: a female is attracted by a male that expresses its aggressiveness by 'song', and when she joins the male, he threatens her.

But threat is only the first phase of courtship. When the female, unlike a male, neither threatens nor fights back, nor flees, the male's reaction passes into a more friendly one. In the black-headed gull the male, after performing the forward display, suddenly turns his head away. The female, which may have adopted the forward posture after alighting, then also turns her head away from the male, and for an instant the two birds are standing facing away from each other. This 'head flagging' is a friendly posture, the opposite of the threat display; the main weapon (the bill) and the main threat colour (the brown face) are concealed instead of

Male black-headed gull, uttering the 'long call'

Male and (not entirely mature) female black-headed gull, going through the 'forward display'

Male and female black-headed gull, 'head flagging'

Female black-headed gull begging for food

26

demonstrated. The gesture means 'I mean no harm', and is understood as such.

Other birds have other ways of expressing this. In many species females adopt the same posture as young birds show when begging for food. Such postures are called 'submissive' or 'appeasement' postures, and usually cause a change in the partner's behaviour. The aggressiveness of the male subsides, and so does the anxiety of the female—females are often afraid of males, which is not surprising in view of the general aggressiveness of male birds in spring. The submissive posture of the female often makes the male react as he would to young birds: he feeds her.

It seems, therefore, that courtship consists of the following behaviour elements: first, the male utters his aggressiveness by song or other far-reaching sounds, or by visual displays, such as the song-flight in skylarks or the beautiful nuptial flight in wood-pigeons. This warns other males off, but attracts the female. When a female joins the male, he—and in some species she too —adopts a threat posture, often with a display of striking colour patterns. When the female shows neither undue aggressiveness nor too much fear after this threat display, the male shows his appeasement ceremony, which produces from the female either the same appeasement posture, or a submissive posture. This opens the way to more friendly relations: the male may feed the female, and, when the birds are getting used to each other, they will mate.

The full course of courtship has only been studied and understood in very few birds. Much more study is certainly needed. There are great differences in behaviour from one species to another. The type of courtship is very closely related to the type of plumage. Since bright colours, such as are used in threat display, are dangerous because they make their bearer conspicuous and therefore vulnerable to predators, most small or defenceless birds have not been able to develop these bright colours, but have instead specialized in coloration which camou-

flages them. In many species, for instance in most ducks, the female alone is camouflaged. This is because the female has to brood the eggs, and her plumage has to protect not only herself but her brood as well. In warblers, wrens, and other species, both male and female are camouflaged, and the males make themselves conspicuous during threat and courtship mainly by movement and voice, a kind of advertisement that can be stopped at once if danger threatens. In other species again, such as shelduck, kingfishers, coots, and others, both sexes are brightly coloured. It is probable that these species need no camouflage because they are distasteful to most predators—another means of defence.

Many species are able to appear gaudy or camouflaged at will. This they do by keeping their bright colours concealed when they are not needed, and flashing them at the female when courting. Spreading of tail and wings often reveals striking patterns even in camouflaged birds. Turkeys, pheasants, and kindred birds have wattles which they can pump full with blood, which makes them swell conspicuously.

Thus the courtship of birds is a complicated affair. In spite of much work done, our understanding of it is still slight. For many years to come it will remain a rewarding subject for study.

A ruff in full spring dress

Black-headed gull collecting nest material

A long-tailed tit building its nest

Black-headed gull building its nest

NEST BUILDING

BIRDS' nests differ very much from one species to another. A nightjar does not build a nest at all; it just lays the eggs on the bare ground. Most other ground-breeding birds make at least a kind of nest cup, though many species, such as terns and many waders, do little more than line the nest cup with shell fragments, pebbles, or grass and similar material. Birds breeding in trees build more elaborate structures, using twigs, roots, grass, moss, or, as in the case of swallows and thrushes, earth or mud. The nest of a pigeon is a rather thin platform of twigs. A mag-pie builds an elaborate nest with a dome and a beautifully lined cup, and wrens construct very tightly-woven domed nests with side entrances. Some tropical song-birds, among them the weaver birds, are true architects and literally weave the materials together.

There are many descriptions of nests in the standard bird books, though good descriptions of the way nests are actually built are extremely rare. Here is an attractive task for patient bird-watchers. Of course, watching a bird building its nest is not as easy as, for instance, watching a bird feeding its young, for many birds are extremely secretive while building, and abandon a nest if too much obvious attention is being paid to it. But that makes it all the more challenging.

First, the pair of birds must select a nest site. Each species has its own needs. Goldcrests, for instance, select dense evergreens with horizontal branches, from which the twigs must hang down at both sides. The nest is then hung up between these twigs. Sparrow hawks nest well below the crown of a tree on a strong fork. Hobbies prefer to nest in the dense crown itself. Grebes always build their floating nests among vegetation, but not too far from the open water, so that they can reach the nest from the water, and can easily slip off into the water.

Most birds construct their nest by astonishingly simple means. I have often watched pairs of long-tailed tits at work. They usually select some fork, either on a strong branch or in a dense bush. They begin by gathering some moss, which they lay down in the fork with some clumsy rubbing movements of the bill. If the moss sticks, the foundations are laid, but often it falls off, and then the tits try again with a new beakful. It often takes quite a time before some of the material holds. After these moss-collecting trips they go in search of material of a quite different kind—spiders' silk. They gather a beakful of this in an amazingly short time. They put it on to the moss, and then, with vertical and horizontal movements of the head, pull it out over the moss and the supporting branches alike, thus weaving the moss to the tree. Moss and silk trips are made in alternating series, and gradually a platform begins to take shape. They then sit on this, and do their further building from the platform. When the structure grows higher, we see a new movement:

bending far forward, the bird tramples with its feet, now and then turning round to face in another direction, thus making a cup in the centre of the platform.

They build on while sitting in the cup, taking turns in doing so, and depositing the new material on the rim. At last the cup is so deep that you can see only the head and the tail of the building bird. Now and then the tits collect lichens, and weave them on the outer surface of the nest, again covering it with spiders' silk. When the nest is almost completed, the birds begin to collect downy feathers to line the cup. There are always plenty of these around: many birds moult in spring; also predators, when they pluck their kills, always leave plenty of downy feathers about. If you happen to have some down at nest-building time, and leave it somewhere in the open, you will almost certainly see various birds come to collect it for their nests.

In many birds, both ground-nesting and tree-nesting species, building is done by sitting on the selected site, depositing the material with the bill either in front or at the side, and making trampling movements now and then to shape the cup. Few species use spiders' silk for binding the material together; most birds just intertwine the twigs or grass by pushing them into the material and making sideways quivering motions until they feel that they stick together

Other birds—swallows, for instance—have different ways of nest-building, and some of these can, with patience and care, be watched through the whole process—a fascinating study.

A scrape of a herring gull

INCUBATION

BIRDS' eggs can develop only if they are kept at a constant and fairly high temperature—about that of the bird's body. Either too low temperatures or too high temperatures kill them. All birds living in our latitude keep the eggs at the right temperature by sitting on them (except the cuckoo, which makes other birds sit on them); in the tropics there are birds which entrust their eggs to the warm earth, or, in slightly colder climates, to a heap of rotting leaves which generate the warmth needed. When the sun gets too hot, these birds may shade the eggs——and the young as long as they are small—by standing above them; but this is different from real brooding.

An egg has a great bulk in comparison with the bird's body. A female cannot, therefore, lay all the eggs of the clutch at once, but produces them in series. Most species lay only one egg a day, or one every second day. In birds such as ducks, who have large clutches, the completion of the clutch takes almost a fortnight. Yet all eggs hatch the same day. This is mainly because the mother duck does not begin to sit until the last egg is laid. Some birds begin to sit on the first or second egg, and then the eggs hatch at long intervals, as do those of harriers and some owls. Other birds do not really incubate the eggs during the first days, but merely

Black-headed gull relieving its mate at the nest

cover them without heating: pigeons, for example, stand guard over the first egg, hiding it from view—the bright white egg being very conspicuous. In true incubation the eggs are brought into contact with one or more naked parts of the skin, the so-called brooding patches, and unless the bird lifts the feathers surrounding these patches and envelops the eggs, they remain cool.

Incubation is by no means always the exclusive task of the female, as it is with domestic fowls. In a few species (such as the phalarope and the dotterel) the male alone broods. But in many species both parents take their turn in sitting. In such cases it is interesting to watch the nest relief. Incubation to the birds is a highly satisfying job, and it often happens that the sitting bird is not very willing to leave the nest, even after several hours of brooding. Nest relief is then a silent but determined struggle between the parents. The relieving partner may come to the nest with various expressions of the intention to sit: it raises the feathers of the abdomen, utters soft calls, bores its head under the sitting bird, or possibly brings some nest material. Usually the sitting bird cannot resist these various hints and gets up. It may then look down into the nest and, seeing the eggs, be stimulated to sit down again. But often it does not get the chance, for the mate, seizing its opportunity, wriggles itself on to the eggs. I have seen this happen with gulls. But sometimes both birds are so eager to sit that in their attempts to force themselves on to the eggs they raise their wings and flap them so violently that you expect the eggs to be crushed.

When a bird settles down on the eggs, it usually brings its bill-tip down between the eggs and carefully shifts them. This is also done from time to time while the bird is sitting. By marking the eggs you can see that this actually results in the eggs being turned round, so that all are uniformly warmed.

Many birds, especially ground-breeding birds, can roll eggs that have been accidentally

Black-headed gull trying to push its mate off the nest

pushed out of the nest back into it. If you take an egg out and put it on the edge of the nest, the bird, when it returns, may not immediately notice the egg. But when it sits on the nest it soon feels what is wrong, and rolls the egg back with its bill. If the egg is too far away to be reached, the bird may stand up, walk towards it, and then roll it under it.

When an egg is about to hatch, the chick inside, by stretching itself repeatedly and slowly turning round, makes a series of cracks, and finally a hole in the shell. With the sharp 'egg-tooth' at the tip of the upper mandible it expands the hole, cracking the shell all the way round, and finally separating a 'lid' from the rest. It then crawls out.

It is worth watching carefully how the parent bird reacts to this. Even before the chick makes the hole, it may begin to call. This perhaps is the stimulus that makes the parent change its behaviour. It frequently looks down into the nest, and it sits more carefully on the eggs than before, standing above them rather than sitting, and keeping the wings slightly lifted. When the eggs have hatched, the parent may pick up and carry away the empty shell, or, as tits do, it may swallow it, in this way recovering part of the lime it originally put into the eggs.

Herring gull with chick   *Herring gull feeding one of its chicks*

WATCHING A

HERRING GULL FAMILY

THE life of a bird family is a particularly attractive drama to watch. I have often spent ten hours at a stretch in a little tent pitched near the nest of a pair of herring gulls. I usually put the tent up about 20 yards from the nest and leave it there for a day so that the birds get used to it, then move it to about 10 yards; a day or two later I bring it to within 2 or 3 yards. When I begin my watch a friend comes with me to the tent, and leaves when I am settled. In that way the birds, concentrating on the retreating enemy, do not suspect that I am still in hiding. Through the peep-hole, camouflaged with some twigs or leaves, I see the parents alight almost within reach.

The chicks, a few days old, were not in the nest when I arrived. But they soon appear from the surrounding dwarf willow bushes where they had been hiding. I had not seen them because of their perfect camouflage, sand-colouring dotted all over with dark patches. Whenever the parents get disturbed and call the alarm call ('gagagagagaga!') the chicks run into cover and crouch.

After the parent birds have stood guard for a while, preening their plumage, one of them—it may be either the father or the mother—stretches its neck, opens its bill widely, and utters a long, wailing call. Immediately the chicks run towards it and begin to peck at its bill-tip. The parent withdraws its head a little, turning and twisting its neck, and after a while its neck shows a curious swelling, which travels upward, and all at once it opens its bill and regurgitates half-digested food. It takes part of this between its bill-tips and presents it to the young, who quickly take and swallow it. The parent takes up some more, and again holds it for the young. When, after some minutes, the young are satisfied, the parent picks up the remainder and swallows it again. Then it thrusts its bill into the sand and wipes it clean.

In warm, sunny weather the young come and sit in the shade of their parent. Unlike other birds, the parent gulls do not stand above the young, spreading their wings, but the chicks have to go to their parents.

The chicks now may do all kinds of interesting things. They preen themselves just as the adults do; they also try to scratch their heads, but often their legs are still so unsteady that they tumble right over while trying to preen. Now and then the chicks peck at insects or at small objects on the ground.

Sometimes the young, especially when they grow large, wander beyond the boundaries of their own territory. Immediately the neighbour, resenting the trespassers, attacks them. How the gulls distinguish between their own and other chicks is marvellous, for it needs close attention and long practice to see any difference. But the gulls never make mistakes.

Now and then the chicks jump up into the air and wave their wings as if they were flying. But the wings are still too tiny to have much effect. It is amusing to watch these youngsters eagerly flapping their wings, jumping up into the air, and falling back helplessly.

A day spent with this family makes one eager to come back on subsequent days and watch the family grow up. After 5 weeks the young are as large as their parents. They have dropped their downy plumage, and developed a dull buff-brown coat of strong, real feathers, different in colour from those of an adult gull. When these full-grown young flap their wings, we can see that they are now as large as those of the parents. They may fly some distance, but still they often return to their base. When the parent feeds them, they assault him so fiercely that they nearly knock him over.

After about 8 weeks the young will leave the parents. Then family ties are loosened, and the young must feed themselves. They need no practice or teaching of any kind; they just go to the shore and feed on molluscs, crabs, and other marine animals washed up by the tide. If they approach their parents or other gulls to beg for food, they are probably chased off. For some time the young gulls, lacking self-confidence, stand continually in the flattened submissive attitude; but this gradually wears off, and within a year they are quite able to hold their own.

Herring gull with two full-grown young

WATCHING A FAMILY OF HOBBIES

A female hobby at the nest, with small young

THE family life of hobbies differs in many respects from that of gulls. Hobbies nest in tree-tops, usually near the edge of the wood. From a simple hide, made of a skeleton of dead branches and covered with moss or bracken, erected at about a hundred yards from the nest, one can, with glasses, overlook both the nest and its surroundings. To see from nearby what happens on the nest a tree-top hide is necessary. I have often built one, tying an old chair high up in a tree, and fixing round it a wire-netting cylinder covered with a camouflage of heather and bracken twined round and through it. From there I have been able, sitting at ease in the tree-top and rocked gently by the wind, to look straight into the alert eyes of the fierce little falcons. Hobbies, unlike herring gulls, have a

Female hobby preparing the prey (bird) for the young

strict division of labour between male and female. The female, who is the larger of the two, stands guard over the young, while the male does the food hunting for the whole family. It may be several hours before he brings a prey to the nest. During these hours the female either broods the young—when they are still small or when it is raining—or sits quietly on a look-out post above the nest.

Suddenly the male calls in the distance, a loud, clear 'kjeekjeekjeekjeekjeekjeekjee!' The female instantly flies off. The male shoots down in a steep glide, carrying its kill in its talons. At some 200 yards from the nest the female meets him and takes his prey from him high in the air. To do this she throws herself on her back in the air under the male, and in an instant the prey is passed from his talons to hers. She flies back at once, and alights on a strong branch near the nest. The young, who have probably heard the male's call or seen the female, begin to beg for food, uttering a long-drawn call. The female now plucks the prey. Holding the small bird in her talons, she bends deeply over it and pulls the feathers off, which float gently down. At the end of the day we can discover from the feathers what kind of bird it was. Now and then she seems to eat a few bits herself. After six or seven minutes she suddenly makes a beautiful curving flight round to the nest and lands. Bit by bit she tears the flesh from the prey's breast, and presents the bits to the clamouring young, who take them from her bill. She makes little attempt to share the food evenly or to see that all get fed; those that do not claim their share just do not get anything. After about ten minutes, when the prey is almost finished, the young stop begging, and the mother hobby finishes the rest. Then she flies back to her look-out.

When the young have grown up and lost their downy plumage, they are able to eat entire song-birds. The female may still try to feed them small bits as before, but the fierce young will not let her. They throw themselves upon the prey as soon as the female lands, almost pushing her over the nest's rim, and usually one of them gets hold of the prey before the others get a chance. Immediately it turns round towards the edge of the nest, covering its booty with drooping wings, and begins to eat. The other young cannot get at it, and have to wait till the next one comes, which means another hour or two.

1117432

Later in the season, though before they leave the nest, the fledglings begin to be interested in moving objects. When they preen themselves, downy feathers float away on the wind, and these they watch, turning and twisting their necks to follow them until they are out of sight. Flies and other insects, and even tits foraging in the tree-tops, are watched intently.

Before the young hobbies can actually fly, they begin to climb round near the nest, soon spending most of their time 'out of doors', returning only when the female brings food to the nest. Gradually they begin to fly, at first just hopping from one branch to another, opening their wings for a large jump. Then they fly to the next tree-top. When the female brings a prey, she may now alight near one of them, and give it the prey there. One day the boldest among them flies to meet her and tries to take the prey over in the air. It usually fails, and the female flies on to one of the other young. Soon they all try to take the prey in the air, and after

a few days they have mastered the trick. But even when they are able to fly hundreds of yards they still cannot get their own food. About ten days after their first flight they begin to catch insects, at first only the sluggish dung beetles, which they capture in flight. On sunny days they circle high in the air following the flying beetles, catching them in one leg and eating them at leisure while gliding, neatly bringing their claws to their bills. They and their parents may spend hours doing this. Usually they just eat the beetles' abdomens and drop the rest. It is weeks before they catch their first bird. They practise this difficult manœuvre day after day, swooping down on each other in what seems to be an exciting game. A brood, fledged in the beginning of August, by the beginning of September are roaming over at least half a mile square; but still they are not catching birds for themselves, and the parents are still bringing them skylarks and swallows in quantity. Soon after this, however, they leave the area and become independent.

The division of labour between the parents is found in all birds of prey. Only when the young are half-grown does the female begin to hunt for them. The hobby differs from most other falcons and hawks, though, in that it is an extremely able insect hunter, and feeds the young with beetles, butterflies, moths, and even dragonflies, and in this male and female take equal shares. It is much more entertaining to watch them during sunny weather than on cold or wet days, for sunny weather brings the insects out, and then every minute or so one of the adult hobbies arrives to feed the young. It is wonderful to see hobbies catch dragonflies. They discover them from a great distance, and fly towards them at tremendous speed, swooping down on them like lightning and catching them with their talons in passing. They then pass the prey to their beak, and glide down to give the hapless insect to the young.

WATCHING A FAMILY OF GREAT TITS

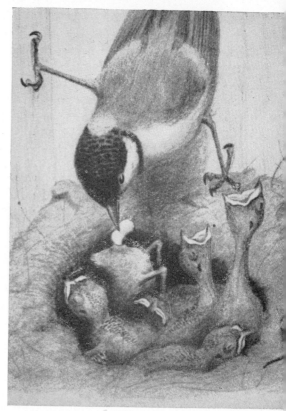

In a nest-box: great tit picking up the faeces of a nestling; other nestlings are still gaping

MANY people have at one time or another watched a blackbird or maybe a skylark feed its young. But few have ever seen what happens inside a nest-box. Yet this is not difficult at all. Ornithologists have developed a simple method for observing tits in nest-boxes by making boxes with ground-glass tops and clear glass backs. The box should be hung about 4 feet above the ground, and the glass windows at first covered, or else the tits might avoid such light boxes. Once a tit has laid eggs in the nest-box, the bird-watcher builds a hide adjacent to the back. Before removing the covering to the glass windows, he attaches a cardboard box to the back of the nest-box, the side touching the glass being open and the other side having two holes for the observer's eyes. This keeps the observer a sufficient distance from the nest so that the tit does not see too much of him. Then, when the covering is removed from the top and back windows, the interior of the box is illuminated, while the observer sits in the dark and cannot be seen.

Instead of building the hide after the nest-box has been occupied, it is possible to build a hide, with one or more nest-boxes attached to it, in the late winter in the hope that the tits will come; though this, of course, involves the risk that no tits settle in the boxes. Such a hide, once the 'stage is set', can be a source of amusement and interest for many weeks.

When the young hatch, a most attractive period begins. Just after hatching they are tiny, with a little grotesque down on the bare pink skin. The little creatures crawl round in the nest on their legs and on their naked, tiny wings, which serve as fore-legs. In the beginning the mother broods them. When she leaves, some nestlings will gape, stretching their necks and opening their beaks wide. The bright yellow edges of their enormous mouths seem to radiate light. When nothing happens, the gaping young subside again. But when the parent comes back with food, up go the beaks again. The parent puts the food neatly down one of the gaping beaks. If the prey is large, such as a caterpillar, the mother may squeeze it, and press its con-

Great tits: a family of almost fledged young

When the baby tits are about ten days old, the plumage begins to show. They are by then quite mobile, and whenever one of the parents comes with food, they all jump up like little Jacks-in-the-box. Still later they begin to flutter their wings whenever they can manage to get some room—which they do by crawling on top of the others. They also begin to be interested in small irregularities in the walls of their tiny room and hammer away at them in the same way that they will later open an insect's cocoon. Still later they begin to climb up to the nest entrance. Fluttering their wings they manage to crawl up to it, cast a quick, interested glance on the world outside, and plunge back into the nest. On the nineteenth or twentieth day after hatching they leave the nest. One works itself up to the entrance, looks round, and hop! off it flies, forty yards or more! Once the first has ventured out, the others follow suit, and within an hour the whole family is outside. There the parents, intensely excited, keep them together by calling incessantly, and soon the family start their journey through the surrounding trees, chattering continually. After fledging, the young are fed for a few weeks more. Yet on the day after leaving the nest they begin to peck at insects themselves, and within a week they manage to find most of their own food.

tents drop by drop into the beaks, as if emptying a tube of toothpaste. She often swallows the tube herself. The begging of the young is so powerful a stimulus to the mother, that a mother tit has even been seen to enter the box with nest material and, being unable to resist the young's gaping, to feed them the moss. The male, arriving immediately afterwards, spent quite a time relieving the young of the indigestible stuff which had got stuck in their throats.

After having fed the young, the parent bird stays for a little while, looking down intently into the nest. Soon one or two of the young bend their heads down, bring their behinds up with a wriggling motion, and suddenly present large white packets of faeces. These the parent picks up and carries off, or even swallows.

Distraction display of a ringed plover

HOW BIRDS RAISE THEIR YOUNG

WE have seen in how widely different ways young herring gulls, young hobbies, and young great tits are raised. Yet these are only three of the two hundred or so species breeding in Britain, many of whom raise their young in further quite different ways. Here are some suggestions of the kind of interesting things which can be seen when watching bird families.

The young of most species of birds are still very dependent in the first days after hatching. The parents must brood them or else they would die of exposure. Even when brooding is no longer strictly necessary, and the parents leave the young uncovered, they may brood them again in an emergency such as a sudden rainstorm. In many species food is brought by the parents, but in others, such as duck and fowl, the young forage for themselves from the beginning. The food of the young often differs from that of the adults; seed-eating finches, for instance, feed their babies, when they are small, with insects.

To answer many questions about bird food we also need to know exactly how much is consumed by a family. An exact study of kind and numbers of prey animals brought during a day, though demanding considerable perseverance, is nevertheless very rewarding. It is astonishing how much young birds eat, when the total quantity eaten is calculated in terms of the bird's own body weight. And when the total ration of a family is calculated, we realize how large the food supply in the environment must be, and how important it is that birds of the same species do not nest too close together.

Keeping the nest clean is another thing that is done in very different ways. While nestling song-birds are dependent on the parents carrying their faeces off, gulls, for instance, and birds of prey, have other means of avoiding dirtying the nest: the young walk back a few steps to the rim of the nest and shoot their faeces out over it. I have repeatedly found sparrow hawks' and hobbies' nests by looking for white splashes on the floor of the wood, which are the consequences of this habit.

Many peculiarities in behaviour are connected with the need of protection from predators. Birds are much more ready to attack predators, even at the risk of their own lives, when they have young than at other times of the year. A friend of mine actually saw a female hobby being killed by a goshawk which it attacked in defence of its nest. Apart from actually attacking, many birds utter alarm calls, and to watch the influence of these calls on the young is very interesting. In many species the alarm call stops the young begging and makes them crouch. I have often taken herring gull chicks into my observation hide, where they were usually quite at ease. But as soon as they heard the 'gagagagaga!' of the adults outside, they crouched at my feet, although they could not have seen the birds that gave the warning.

Many species lure predators away from the nest by 'distraction displays', such as fluttering and limping before the enemy to turn its attention away from the nest—as described on p. 19. We still know very little about the influence of these displays on predators. It seems that birds of prey, stoats, and other carnivores, and even snakes, are misled, and are tempted to run after the parent instead of searching for the nest.

Another type of defence is concealment. Behaviour and coloration are both adapted to this in the most minute and amazing details. Birds such as pheasants and nightjars, whose eggs are relatively conspicuous but who themselves have a beautifully camouflaged plumage, tend to crouch on the nest until you can almost, or even actually, touch them. Oystercatchers, gulls, and terns are conspicuous themselves, but their brood is camouflaged. Such species, instinctively relying on the camouflage of the brood, leave the nest at the slightest disturbance. Grebes, which have almost white eggs, leave the nest as gulls do, but cover the eggs with weeds before slipping off. In species where the male bird is much more conspicuously coloured than the female—red-backed shrikes, for instance—the males approach the nest much more cautiously, reaching it through dense cover, whereas the female flies in from the open. Having fed the young, however, the male flies straight out into the open with no attempt at concealment—the assumption being that the predator is more inclined to follow the bird than stop to see where it has come from. Some more intelligent birds, however, such as carrion crows, will watch for a bird to leave its nest and then prey upon the brood.

In social birds, particularly those whose young wander about, we might ask whether each pair of parents manages to remain in touch with their own young, and to feed them and not any young they meet. Species such as geese, terns, and some gulls always seem to know their own young. Some species stay on their territory with their brood; others wander about with the brood. Young sandwich terns often form large groups, and it has been often thought that the young in such a nursery or 'crèche' are fed indiscriminately by all the parents concerned. However, later in the season, when old and young migrate together, each old bird can be seen to feed one or two young (in all probability its own offspring) while being indifferent to others, however much they beg for food, and therefore it seems unlikely that feeding in the crèche is really indiscriminate. Even with penguins, where the crèche-system has been reported to exist, the evidence is not entirely convincing, and a closer study of this remarkable phenomenon would certainly be rewarding.

Do bird parents teach their young? If so, what do they teach them? We still know only a little about this. One thing is certain: they do not teach them how to fly. Birds reared by human foster parents fly just as well as birds reared by their own parents, provided they are kept under the right conditions. And I have never heard of pigeon breeders who taught their birds how to fly. Even the 'practising' which young birds do while still in the nest is not real practising; experiments have shown that young pigeons and other birds that are prevented from using their wings at all until they are full grown will fly just as well as birds which have 'practised'.

But birds do learn other things. It is probable that some species of song-birds have to learn their own species' song. Many learn to react to the calls of their parents. A Finnish biologist once exchanged the eggs of a turnstone and a redshank, and when the young had hatched, he noticed that the young turnstones did not react to the calls of their real parents, but to those of their foster parents. They can only have learnt this. In other species, the recognition of the parents' calls seems to be innate.

A pied flycatcher with aluminium and coloured rings

BIRTHS AND DEATHS IN A POPULATION

ONE pair of birds can raise three, five, or even twelve young—depending on the species—but, although a species may be a little commoner one year than another, apart from abnormal occurrences it rarely decreases or increases in numbers over a long period, the numbers fluctuating round an average. This means that on the average each bird, when it dies, must be replaced by one and only one younger bird; of all the young produced by, say, a pair of great tits, only two survive until the parents die. Of course, this does not apply in every case; one pair may live longer, another pair may die before its young have fledged. But on the average, births and deaths in a population must be balanced.

We do not know why so many birds die, nor what they die of. One way of finding out is to count birds, and painstaking and slow as this

work is, it has been done in a number of cases. It is relatively easy to count large, conspicuous birds, such as seagulls, or herons, or rooks, but much more difficult with small birds. Many of these, however, help us by singing in spring, and on the whole a singing male means a breeding pair—although allowance must be made for birds that remain unmated. Most of such counts have been restricted to a small area, such as a 200-acre wood; but some birds have been counted all over the country, and of a few species we have more or less exact figures of the world population. Thus it is known that there are about 4,000 breeding pairs of grey herons in Great Britain, and that there are some 7,000 pairs in Holland.

Such counts have to be repeated at various times of the year, and have to be continued over many years. The counts that have been done mostly concern resident species. All species studied so far show great fluctuations in the course of the year. Naturally, numbers are greatest in early summer, just after the breeding season, and decline again until the beginning of the next breeding season, when they are about back to the level of the previous year. With resident birds, this reduction must be due to mortality.

We can learn something about births and deaths by studying nesting success and life-span of individual birds. Each bird of the area to be studied is trapped and ringed with its own combination of two, three, or even more rings of different colours. Thus we can mark many birds individually. Each bird is followed throughout its life, and each observation entered in the files.

If we follow such a ringed population through a number of years, marking each new young bird before it fledges, we can find out how long they live on the average. This varies from one species to another; in most song-birds studied it is between 2 and 3 years, although some individuals have been known to live 10 years or longer. In larger birds the span of life is often

A tragedy on the sea-shore: dying oystercatchers on the frozen beach during a spell of severe frost in Holland

longer. If the birds live relatively long, this means that the renewal of the population is relatively slow, and that there are, at any given moment, few young birds compared with old ones. In short-lived species, many young must reach maturity and replace the adults much faster. If we ring a sufficiently large population and follow it long enough, our figures will tell us all these things.

When in this way we have settled who dies and when, we have to find the actual mortality factors. So far as we know at present these may be food shortage, diseases, predators, or behaviour of the birds themselves. In severe winters it is more usually the food shortage than the cold itself that kills so many birds. Spring fighting, which forces some males into less suitable habitats, may be the cause of low nesting success, at least in some years.

After a deep fall in numbers, for instance in a cold winter, a sharp rise in numbers usually occurs in the next two or three breeding seasons. But after that the population remains more or less stable. The sharp rise is not due to the birds laying more eggs, but to more young birds surviving. This leads to the conclusion that the percentual mortality is not always the same, but that it is dependent on the density of the population. Therefore, there must be mortality factors which are 'density-dependent' which kill a higher proportion when birds are numerous than when they are rare. The regulation of numbers in a population obviously must be due to such density-dependent factors, for a factor such as severe frost, which kills off the same percentage (say the 80 least hardy individuals out of every 100) irrespective of the size of the total population, can never make a population fluctuate round an average.

There has been much discussion about which factors are density-dependent and which are not, but, as is so often the case, this indicates that our exact knowledge is still insufficient. A great deal of work needs to be done on this interesting problem. We need more ornithologists of the persevering kind—people willing to spend years on a thorough, difficult, but rewarding study of bird populations.

THE DIET OF HAWKS

IN the first chapter we saw that a sparrow hawk, after having captured a tit, went to a dense pine plantation to pluck and eat it, littering the ground with the pluckings. The sparrow hawk, as other birds, has its home area, and it probably returns to the same place regularly to pluck and eat its prey. Such a place, if you can find it, gives a unique opportunity for studying the hawk's diet, for there you can find the remains, neatly spread out, of all the different birds that have fallen victims to the hawk. Some of these birds can be easily recognized from the remains. Black wing- and tail-feathers, greyish black-tipped downy feathers, and, if the hawk has not been disturbed while plucking, a bright orange bill cannot be mistaken: they have belonged to a blackbird. The beautiful black-and-white feathers of a great spotted woodpecker are also easily labelled. A jay reveals itself by its hand-some blue hand-coverts. A turtle dove has very conspicuous dark, white-tipped tail-feathers and lovely cinnamon back-feathers. Other birds, such as tits, warblers, pipits, flycatchers, may be less easy to identify, but if the pluckings are collected into an old envelope and taken back to be compared with the stuffed birds in, per-haps, the collection of a local museum, they can often be identified. If the finds are then arranged and mounted on sheets of thin cardboard and labelled, they serve as a reference collection for later use. Unless they are sprayed with an insecticide, however, various insects will destroy them.

Sparrow hawks much more often catch some species than others: the sparrow hawk's hunting method seems to be especially effective with thrushes and chaffinches, whereas coal tits seem to be much more difficult to catch, so that even in areas where they are abundant it is very seldom that their pluckings are found.

At first inclination it seems most interesting to find as many diverse species as possible, and to collect rare species. You will be excited to find the yellow wing-feathers and the tiny red facial-features of a goldfinch. I still remember finding a bright blue plucking, which could be seen on the brown carpet of pine needles from a great distance. It had belonged to a hapless budgerigar!

But in course of time, especially as the chance of finding new prey species decreases, other in-teresting aspects to your detective work become more apparent, which the hunt for rarities and spectacular species may have prevented you from seeing. If you collect pluckings in different localities, probably made by different individual hawks, you will see that their diets differ. Even in one locality the diet of the same bird may change in the course of time. This emphasizes the intricate relationships between a bird's food and its environment. The differences may be due to differences in availability: a sparrow hawk living in the woods will certainly have fewer house sparrows on its list than one which lives near human habitations. But there may also be differences between the various in-dividual sparrow hawks. Males, which are much smaller than females, probably kill fewer jays and other large species than do females. But even the diet of two females living in the same kind of habitat may be very different. Does this point to a difference in personal taste? Or has one of them just discovered, say, a colony of starlings which the other female has failed to find?

Opposite are some lists of pluckings found in different localities. Of course, we do not know how many hawks had killed these birds, nor how many birds are killed each day; but these lists do tell us in what proportion various prey species are taken.

The goshawk has much the same hunting methods as the sparrow hawk. Being much larger, it captures larger prey species. Also, it

Where a goshawk plucked a little owl

Plucking of a great spotted woodpecker by sparrow hawk, arranged for demonstration

kills relatively more mammals such as rabbits. At present it is extremely rare in Britain, but it might well increase again now that more and more people begin to realize that 'vermin' are entitled to their little share in our natural resources.

PLUCKINGS FOUND IN VARIOUS LOCALITIES

Food of sparrow hawks near a town in winter		*Food of sparrow hawks in sand-dune country on one of the Frisian islands in winter*		*Food of goshawks in Holland*	
Woodcock	1			Rabbit	90
Fieldfare	1			Red squirrel	46
Missel thrush	1	Waterrail	4	Other mammals	12
Song thrush	2	Woodcock	2	Pigeons (mainly	
Redwing	5	Wood pigeon	1	wood-pigeon)	230
Blackbird	8	Fieldfare	14	Jay	68
Robin	6	Song thrush	3	Partridge	36
Woodlark	4	Redwing	1	Green woodpecker	13
Skylark	1	Blackbird	2	Other birds	78
Great tit	5	Robin	2		—
Blue tit	1	Skylark	2		576
Starling	6	Starling	17		
Chaffinch	14	Bullfinch	1		
Brambling	1		—		
Siskin	4		49		
Linnet	2				
House sparrow	23				
Tree sparrow	7				
Greenfinch	5				
	—				
	97				

A long-eared owl on its nest; flashlight photograph

OWLS' PELLETS

A FASCINATING way of studying the food of predators is the analysis of owls' pellets. All owls swallow their prey after very little preparation. Small mammals are often swallowed whole; birds are partly plucked, so that the larger feathers are to be found under the tree where the owl has done the plucking. These feathers are much more difficult to collect than those left by sparrow hawks because the owl does not come to the ground to do the plucking, and so the feathers are often blown along and spread before they reach the ground. But an owl's stomach does not digest bones, and these, with some feathers and hairs, are regurgitated in the form of 'pellets'. Some owls, such as the long-

eared owl and the barn owl, deposit their pellets at their roosts; the tawny owl is less co-operative and drops them all over its territory.

By collecting the pellets and carefully pulling them to pieces, you find the bones of the prey animals, which can often be recognized, particularly by their skulls. However, pellets do not give all the information we need. For, as some prey animals do not leave any recognizable traces in them, there is the risk of missing part of the evidence. Direct observation of what owls eat and bring to their young is always necessary in order to make really complete diet data.

The collection and systematic analysis of owl pellets results in many interesting discoveries. The diet of a barn owl, for example, is discovered to be strikingly different from that of a long-eared owl: the barn owl eats masses of shrews, whose handsome skulls with the red-tipped teeth can be easily recognized. The other owls prefer mice and voles, and a glance at the pictures will show how these can be distinguished.

Sometimes you may find in a pellet a bird's ring, such as are used for the marking of birds. Or you may find a vole skull with one molar missing; since upper and lower jaws are often found in the same position as they have in the intact animal, you may be able to see that the molar opposite the missing tooth has grown to an excessive length because it was not worn off as it should have been. Very rarely you will find the digits and the skull of a bat.

An analysis of the food of long-eared owls which I carred out years ago, and in the course of which I found about 23,000 prey animals in the pellets investigated, showed nicely the influence of environment on the diet. Voles are among the animals which show marked fluctuations in numbers from year to year. Consequently the percentage of voles in the owls' food in the first winter when voles were abundant was much higher than in the next winter, when they were relatively scarce everywhere. When I collected the pellets of one brood of owls at short intervals all through the summer, I found a marked rise in the percentage of voles taken at the moment when the corn was cut. The obvious explanation was that this robbed the voles in the owls' hunting territory of much of their protective cover, and made them more vulnerable to attack. This study has now taught us a great deal about owls' food; but this varies with the region, and many regions have not yet been searched for pellets.

Analysis of owls' pellets may tell us more about the mammal fauna of a given locality than we could otherwise collect in a lifetime. It is relatively easy to find pellets, but it is difficult to find small mammals alive in nature, since they live concealed and are mostly nocturnal.

In Holland, where this kind of work has been done by many keen amateurs, pellet analysis often proved mammals to be existing in localities where they were unknown before. It was found, for instance, that the Frisian island of Texel harbours only one kind of vole, *Microtus ratticeps*, which has a very local and patchy distribution on the mainland, whereas the vole *Microtus arvalis*, common on the mainland, does not occur on Texel at all.

Pellets under a roost of a long-eared owl

THE TOLL LEVIED BY PREDATORS

WHEN you collect pellets or pluckings you may be struck by the enormous numbers of prey animals that fall victims to predators: it appears that predators must be an important mortality factor for the prey species concerned. Yet in order to judge this, we should know not only how many birds are killed by predators, but what proportion of the total mortality of those species is due to predators. This problem can be solved, and our study of the food of hawks or

Some skulls found in owl pellets
Top: insect-eating song-bird (left), bird ring, seed-eating song-bird. Middle: bank vole (left), jaw and digit of bat (top centre), jaws of shrew and water shrew (lower centre), Norwegian rat. Bottom: jaws of two kinds of voles (left), skull of Microtus ratticeps *(centre), skull and jaw of house mouse (right)*

owls may be the first step towards a solution. But a great amount of work is needed before we shall be able to give the answer.

In order to tackle this job we must first find out how large the hunting area of the predator is. Since it is impossible to follow a sparrow hawk on its hunting trips, we have to use an indirect method. In a particular area where sparrow hawks were common in the neighbouring woods, and where house sparrows were living in some small villages only, it was found that sparrows were represented in the diets of those hawks nesting less than 2 miles from a village, and not in those of the others. Clearly the hawks living farther than 2 miles from a village did not visit it at all. From data like this the size of the hawk's hunting area can be deduced.

Another method has been applied to owls living mainly on voles. The voles of a large area were trapped alive and provided with a numbered ring round the leg. Retrapping the voles at monthly intervals and reading their ring numbers showed that they did not roam very far from where they had been trapped. Since many of these voles were caught by owls, a study of the ring numbers found in the owls' pellets revealed the extent of the owls' hunting areas.

Our next task would be the assessment of the total population of the prey species selected for our study within the hunting area. We have already seen on page 40 how that can be done in the case of birds. With voles, another type of evidence may be used. The number of voles in a given area may be called n. As many as possible are trapped, ringed, and then released. A month later the process is repeated. If on the first occasion 50 voles have been ringed, there will be in the area 50 ringed voles and $n-50$ unringed ones. On the second occasion, chances being equal, the catch should be in the proportion of $50/(n-50)$ ringed and unringed voles. If, in fact, the catch is 3 ringed and 21 unringed voles, then, since 21 is seven times 3, $n-50$ must be seven times 50; in other words there are 350 unringed voles, or 400 voles altogether. If this process is repeated a number of times to eliminate chance variations, from their combined results a fairly accurate assessment of the vole population can be reached.

We need to know the total mortality of this prey population for a given span of time. Since it is, as we have seen, impossible to find all animals that have died, we must again apply an indirect method. This is possible since we know that on the average a species remains constant in numbers. Therefore the mortality in the course of a year must equal the number of births in that year. We therefore determine the number of births. Again, this has to be done over a number of years, because the birth-rate fluctuates round an average.

Now we know, with a reasonable degree of accuracy, the total mortality of the prey population in the hunting area of the predator. From a study of the predator's pluckings or pellets, we know what proportion our prey species occupies in its entire diet. But since we cannot possibly claim that we find the remains of every single prey the predator has taken—in fact we usually find only a small proportion of all prey animals—we must find how much the predator takes in total, and then compute, from the proportional figures, the actual number of our prey animals taken. This last figure can then be compared with the total mortality, and then at last we know what part of the mortality is due to the predator studied.

Such a study is clearly a formidable task. Practical difficulties of all kinds may be in our way, and it is not astonishing that a complete study of this kind can only be undertaken in particularly favourable species, and that even at the best it takes years to get reliable figures. Yet for our insight into the economy of wild life such work is important, and several of such studies are being carried out now. Some results have already been obtained. We know, for instance, that in one area sparrow hawks are responsible for about 50 per cent. of the mortality of sparrows within their hunting territories. But of other small birds in the same area they took a much smaller proportion. For instance, of the total mortality of chaffinches and great tits, no more than 20 per cent. were due to sparrow hawks, and their part in the mortality of coal tits did not amount to more than a few per cent. These figures apply only to part of the year.

Of course, with the computation of these average percentual figures the job is not done. What we have to find out is whether these predators are 'density-dependent' mortality factors or not. That means that we shall have to find out how their diet changes with changes in the available numbers of the prey animals. A truly density-dependent factor increases its percentual tax when numbers go up. And, although we have but a few very meagre facts on this problem, it looks as if at least birds of prey cannot bring the percentual total up. It is true that they take greater numbers of an abundant prey species than of one that is rare, and that the total numbers taken of a given species increase with an increase in that species' density. But the percentage taken of the whole probably goes down, and the prey species quickly outgrows the predators.

Thus there is still much uncertainty about the part played by birds of prey in nature. The only way to gain an insight in such matters is continued, detailed, quantitative study.

HOW DO BIRDS RECOGNIZE PREDATORS?

WHEN one watches birds in the field regularly, one cannot miss occasionally seeing birds of prey, or stoats, or other predators. It is always worth watching the birds around when one of these appears. As we have already seen, different species react in different ways; many species even have more than one way of reacting. Partridges may crouch when they see a harrier pass overhead. House sparrows hop about in the bush just over a cat in the garden, uttering their alarm call. Many birds mob predators: starlings, wagtails, and many other song-birds, for example, gather in a dense flock above a sparrow hawk and, calling excitedly, swoop down on it. Waders on wide mud flats or marshes fly up when a peregrine appears and execute their wonderful manœuvres in dense flocks, often trying to rise above their enemy. Duck, when really scared, plunge down into the water.

Swallows fleeing from young hobbies at play

It is amazing that birds can recognize predators so surely, even when they are still at a great distance. It is noticeable that the same species of predator does not always elicit the same response. Many birds are not afraid of and may even attack boldly a peregrine dozing quietly on a lonely post on the fields, while they may be thrown into a frenzy by the sight of the same peregrine flying fast and determinedly over the same field. A pigeon, however, flying over at the same speed will cause those same birds to give scarcely a second glance.

The field watcher can get an idea of how birds recognize predators by comparing situations that call forth a response with those that do not, and also by registering 'errors': birds occasionally show the typical predator-response when there is no enemy in sight. Usually, in such cases, they have reacted erroneously to another bird. I once watched two fully fledged hobbies catching insects about 500 yards up in the air. Far below them, at about 200 yards above the ground, a flock of migrating swallows were hunting for insects. They did not mind the falcons above them. Suddenly, the hobbies stopped catching dung beetles, and began to play, swooping down at each other, as young hobbies often do, with movements much the same as those of adult hobbies chasing small birds. Although the hobbies stayed as high up as before and paid no attention to the swallows below, the swallows immediately got into a panic and dashed down. It must have been, therefore, the characteristic movements of the hobbies that scared them. Still more striking are the many occasions I have observed when flocks of waders panicked because a newly arriving godwit, redshank, or black-headed gull fell down from the sky like a stone, as they often do in good weather. This reminded them of the drop of a hunting peregrine.

In other cases it is clear that the shape of a bird rather than its movements stimulates an erroneous response. When swifts arrive in the beginning of May, many birds watch them suspiciously and even show full predator responses to them. This mistaken response is seen only in the first days after the swifts' arrival; the birds soon get used to them. Now a swift resembles a falcon, particularly a hobby, in shape and flight, and there can scarcely be any doubt that the similarity in shape causes the commotion.

The conclusion that both movements and shape are the characteristics by which birds recognize a bird of prey can easily be tested by simple experiments. A colleague and I once did some such tests. We fixed a wire between two tree-tops above a lawn where we kept tame birds—goslings, ducklings, and young fowl of various kinds. Along this wire we could pull models made of cardboard and cut in various shapes. The birds on the lawn reacted to only certain of these models. Those frightening our birds all had bird shape, and they all had short necks. Those with long necks were without effect. We made one model that had a short protuberance at one end, and a long one at the other end. Neither had a very definite shape,

each could act as a tail or as a head, dependent on the direction of movement. It produced predator response when pulled in one direction, but was considered quite harmless by the birds when pulled in the other direction. These tests indicated that the short neck was the main aspect of a predator's shape to which the birds reacted.

The type of movement is also important. Once we pulled a large circular disk along the wire, but our birds paid no attention. Then, when a gust of wind threw it off and it came tumbling down, there was a panic.

Geese, whose main enemy among the birds of prey is the white-tailed eagle, become alarmed whenever any object moves slowly overhead. They reacted in our experiments not only to a model of an eagle, but also to floating downy feathers, and to jackdaws and pigeons as soon as these began to soar. Even a large aircraft very high up had the same effect. All these objects have in common that they move slowly in relation to their size, as eagles do.

Other observers have tried to find out how birds recognize owls. Because many birds 'mob' an owl when it sits on its roost, recognition of the owl can be tested by presenting birds with stuffed owls and various simplified models. It seems that the plumage, and its colour pattern, is one of the recognizable characteristics. Mammals such as stoats provide other stimuli again; their fur seems to be frightening in itself.

It is great fun to try to carry out such experiments, many of which can be done in a country garden. Although we are almost certain that the means by which birds recognize predators differ from one species to another, our knowledge is still very inadequate. With a little attention, ingenuity, and perseverance anyone can gather information that may throw light on this problem.

A goose family scared by a cardboard 'sparrow hawk'
(above, right)

WHY DO BIRDS
BEHAVE AS
THEY DO? – 1

WE have seen that birds do a great number of things which are useful to them, that is, which help them to survive, or to raise their young and thus perpetuate their kind. Studying the behaviour of birds from this point of view and discovering the ends served by their activities leads us to wonder what makes birds do all these things. Birds, of course, do not do things for the same kind of reasons which would lead us to do similar things, namely by 'using their brains' and either thinking out or learning the best ways of dealing with the outside world. Often birds do very stupid things, and this leads us to realize that birds are not really clever enough to think out, say, how to build a nest. It is this strange contrast between the stupidity which a bird shows at one moment and its apparent cleverness at another which makes us wonder what a bird's 'cleverness' really is. When a blackbird sees a hawk and gives the alarm call which makes her young crouch in the nest, we begin to wonder whether the blackbird really knows that if she does not call, her young will draw the hawk's attention by their incessant movements, and will probably be killed. Close observation certainly does not raise our respect for a bird's mental abilities, as the following examples may show.

A female cuckoo, as we all know, lays her eggs in a nest of a song-bird. When the young cuckoo hatches, which it usually does some time in advance of the eggs of its foster parents, it wriggles itself with its back under the eggs, and by crawling backwards towards the nest's rim throws them out. Or, if the other eggs have already hatched, it throws the tiny, naked young out so that they lie quite helpless on the nest's

rim and soon cool off. The parent bird, instead of taking its own nestlings back into the nest—which it could do easily—broods and feeds the cuckoo while its own young are dying under its eyes. It makes no attempt to feed the dying young because they are not in the nest and because they do not gape for food. Experiments have shown that a young song-bird, in order to be accepted by the parents, must be in the nest and must gape for food. Clearly the parent song-bird has not the slightest idea that the function of its parental activities is to raise its own offspring, and not a parasite which has just murdered its young. We shall see later that the parental behaviour of birds is caused not by 'knowledge' of its effect, but rather by certain stimulations from within and from without to which the birds react 'blindly'.

Here is another instance of stupid behaviour. A gull or a tern, startled from its nest, may knock one of the eggs out of the nest. On returning to the nest, the bird sees the egg, and bringing its bill behind it tries to roll it back, carefully balancing it on the narrow underside of the lower mandible. This is a difficult thing to do, for the egg easily slips away sideways, and the bird may have to try again and again before it finally manages to bring it back into the nest cup. The bird could do the job much more efficiently if it swept the egg back with the extended wing or used one of its webbed feet. But this does not occur to the bird; it just 'has' this reaction.

Again, when herring gulls find food on the shore, such as a cockle, which is too hard for them to crush, they take it in their bill, fly up into the air, and drop it from ten or fifteen yards up. If there happens to be rock below, the cockle smashes, and all is well; but often enough they drop it on mud, or even in the water. So little do they understand the purpose of their action and so little do they learn by experience that they will try again and again to crush the shell on the mud, while not far away there is solid rock.

Such facts show that birds may do things

which work well, and therefore seem clever in ordinary circumstances, but as soon as something slightly unusual happens they are at a loss. They show that birds have little knowledge of why they do all the clever things they do and that they are often unable to learn. However, it would be untrue to say that they have no knowledge whatsoever or that they cannot learn at all. Some birds show traces of what we call intelligent behaviour. Crows, for instance, have the same habit as gulls of dropping hard food in order to crack it; but unlike the gulls, they can learn to avoid soft soil, and to do their 'bombing' on rock, or concrete road, or ice.

Crows and their relatives often bury surplus food so that they can return to it later when they need it. A jackdaw, however, will bury its hoard with other jackdaws looking on, who steal the food immediately the owner has gone. This may happen again and again, it never occurring to the jackdaw that it is useless to bury food while others are looking on. Ravens, however, without doubt the most intelligent birds of their tribe, will not conceal their food when they are being watched. They just wait or go somewhere else where they are not observed. In other respects, too, ravens show traces of understanding the 'why' of things. A reliable observer has reported that he saw one of his tame ravens, while having a bath, accidentally splash its brother who was sitting nearby. Immediately the brother flew down and chased the offender away. When we remember the automatic behaviour of most birds, we realize how extraordinary it was that the brother raven should know that the other was the cause of the splashing.

Nevertheless, birds do most things without having to learn them. Birds raised by man without ever having seen other birds build excellent nests, feed their young, apply all the methods of their kind to find and get food, and so on. Many birds can learn, it is true, but their learning is primitive, and is only done in special circumstances.

Immature herring gull dropping shellfish

WHY DO BIRDS BEHAVE AS THEY DO? – 2

Young blackbirds gaping as a reaction to a human hand

FROM our observations in the foregoing chapter we have been able to conclude that knowledge and learning do not determine most types of bird behaviour. What then, does make birds behave as they do? Many people think that this is an insoluble problem and that we shall never be able to understand, let alone predict, the behaviour of animals. Other people try to work out theories, thinking hard about the animals' minds and personalities without, perhaps, spending enough time in watching what does happen. It is true, of course, that one has to use one's brains; but it is above all necessary to observe what birds do before thinking out theories. By patient use of our eyes and ears together with a little common sense we can learn a great deal.

We often see that birds react to things that happen in their environment—for instance, that many birds crouch, or call an alarm, or go into cover when they see a bird of prey. We have seen that parent song-birds feed their young when they gape, but do not feed them when for some reason they fail to do so. Clearly such things happening in the outside world are seen or heard by them, and this makes them react. In the language of the scientist, their behaviour in such cases is a reaction to stimuli. The birds receive such stimuli through their sense organs —eyes, ears, and the like. In studying this, we must never forget that the sense organs of a bird need not be functioning in exactly the same way as ours. Most birds have a very poor sense of smell, but their eyes are better than ours: they can see things at great distances.

On page 48 we saw that when a bird reacts to a bird of prey in the air, it does not react to everything it can see of the predator: it does not bother to look whether the bird of prey has, for instance, sharp talons or a curved beak; it just looks at the short neck and then bolts. Yet we know that with their keen eyesight they could easily see those details, and that they need not react to our cardboard dummy if they only 'had a better look'. Now this seems to be a general rule: birds react often to a few 'sign stimuli' and ignore all other aspects of the situation, however well they can observe them. And when the sign stimuli are there, they must react, even if all other details of the situation could tell them that they need not.

It is reasonably easy to find out to what sign stimuli a bird reacts in a given case. When watching blackbirds feeding their young I was struck by the promptness with which the young gaped as soon as the parent alighted on the nest. When, in an interval while the parents were away, I went to the nest and moved my hand near it, the young gaped towards my hand! Clearly the hand gave some stimuli normally given by the parent. I then made some simple models and showed them to the young. By comparing which models made them gape and

52

which did not, I could find to what stimuli the young reacted. A moving flat cardboard disk made them gape equally whether it was black, as the parent bird, or white. Neither colour nor size nor shape mattered, but it had to move; a motionless imitation of a blackbird did not make them gape at all. Also, it had to be above the nestlings' eyes. When I moved my model below that plane, they looked at it but did not gape. Thus, by these experiments I concluded that the birds gaped in reaction to anything that was above eye level and that moved. In nature, of course, the parent produces exactly this stimulus, for it alights high enough and always moves when it does so.

On page 32 we saw that herring gull chicks peck at their parent's bill-tip when they are hungry. Now a herring gull's bill is yellow, with a bright red patch at the tip of the lower mandible. If you show chicks a flat cardboard model of the head of a herring gull, they will eagerly peck at it. If next you show them a similar model but without a red patch, the chicks will peck only half-heartedly. The red patch obviously gives them a strong stimulus. If next you give them a model with the red patch but with a green or a white bill instead of a yellow one, the young peck as eagerly as at the first model. The colour of the bill, therefore, does not matter to them. Similarly, if you show them a model with a black head instead of a white one, but again with a red patch on the bill, they peck equally well at either head. Head colour, therefore, also does not give a stimulus, but only the red patch. The head need not be there at all: the chicks will peck just as well at a mere bill as at a complete head. You can easily show that such herring gull chicks cannot have learnt this. You can hatch some gull chicks under a sitting hen or in an incubator, with no parent herring gull from which they could learn where the food comes from. Yet such chicks peck as eagerly at our models as the chicks in the wild.

From such tests and others we can conclude that a bird often reacts instinctively to certain simple stimuli without ever having learnt to. But this is not the whole story. Just after a gull chick has been fed, it will not beg for food, even from its own parents. Therefore, the internal state, the physical need, has also a say in the matter. We still do not know much of the internal states that determine what an animal will do. But many scientists are busy finding out, and already understand enough to know how extremely complicated these things are.

A herring gull chick gaping at a cardboard model of an adult's head

THE 'LANGUAGE'
OF BIRDS

BIRDS are social beings—that is, they gather in groups which often do things together. The group can be large, consisting of thousands of individuals, or only one pair and then the family of that pair. Doing things together requires communication of some kind. We have already encountered examples of such communication. We saw that the parent herring gull, by uttering a long-drawn, wailing call, stimulates the young to come and beg for food, or by alarm calls makes the young crouch. Such calls, therefore, act as a kind of language; they influence other individuals. But the 'language' of birds consists also of visual signs which birds give each other. The attack posture of one bird causes its opponent to withdraw. The gaping of nestling song-birds stimulates the parents to feed them. Special colour markings may also convey a message, as does the red patch on the herring gull's bill-tip. Often a gesture serves to show off such a conspicuous signal, as, for example, when a male chaffinch shows off his white epaulets, and a robin its red breast. Other chaffinches and robins are frightened by these displays. By watching what gestures, calls, and displays birds perform and how other birds of the same species react to them, we learn to understand how birds regulate their social life.

What kind of messages does this 'language' convey, and how does it compare to our speech? Most often a call, gesture, or other signal means no more than 'do this now!' A herring gull's alarm call makes the young crouch or, if they are half-grown, run to shelter and crouch there. It therefore says 'crouch now!', but cannot tell them where to crouch. I once saw this demonstrated beautifully while I was watching gulls from a hide. The young gulls had become so accustomed to the hide that they had begun to use it as cover, sliding under it and crouching inside whenever they heard the alarm—even if I was there. One day the parent saw me make a slight movement behind my peep-hole and at once called the alarm, walking away from my hide and looking back at it. The young reacted promptly, stretched their necks, and ran towards their accustomed hiding place, which happened to be the danger which had stimulated the mother's alarm call!

Though most signals merely convey this one message, 'do this now!', many others indicate some directive as well—usually of the simple kind, 'come here!' or 'go away!' We have seen that song attracts females and repels males. Song, therefore, gives these directives. The red patch of the herring gull's bill not only stimulates begging but also directs the young to the bill-tip. If, for example, we show the young a model with the red patch at the bill's base instead of at the tip, the young will aim there.

But beyond this 'here' or 'away' the directives rarely go. A signal can, however, sometimes be used to show another bird a certain locality. The male kestrel, like other birds that breed in holes, selects the nest hole, and therefore he has to show the female where she can lay her eggs. He does so by performing a sort of ceremony in front of her: with wings held up in a V-posture and tail spread, he sails towards the hole. She follows him, and thus arrives at the right place. Once she is there, the hole itself provides the stimulus which informs her, 'this is a suitable

A male redstart showing nest hole to a female

54

A threat posture of a male herring gull: a 'gesture' understood by all other herring gulls

hole'. The redstart and the pied flycatcher carry out similar ceremonies. It is certainly no accident that the male kestrel has this bright blue tail, the male redstart a red tail, and the male pied flycatcher such a brightly chequered back: these colours make the ceremonial flights very conspicuous to the females.

Bird language, therefore, is extremely simple —merely making the other bird do a certain thing, do it now, go towards the caller or away from it, and, perhaps, in rare cases, making it go 'there'. It is amazing to see how on these simple principles birds manage to 'run' their communities.

Another point of difference between bird language and human speech is the fact that most birds do not have to learn their language. The tendency to give certain calls in certain situations, for instance, the alarm call in the presence of a predator, is inborn, and so is the tendency in the other bird to react in the correct way.

This language is not unlike one kind of language which humans use. We need not learn to assume an angry look nor to interpret it in others. The human baby does not learn to cry but does so right at birth; and a normal mother does not have to learn what it means; she knows that a crying baby wants care of some kind.

So far as we know, the calling bird has no 'knowledge' of the end which the call has to serve, but, as in other instances of bird behaviour, reacts 'blindly' to certain internal and external stimuli. It may have a dim knowledge of the ends served, but certainly not sufficient to make it give the correct signal. A single, captive bird, for instance, will give its alarm call whenever it is distressed, for instance by a cat, even though it could know that its call is purposeless since there are no other birds present to react to it. It just calls because it is stimulated to do so by the recognized stimulus—the presence of the cat.

A complicated track of a kestrel. At the left-hand bottom corner it has swooped down on a pine cone, carried it to the right, where it stood for a while and dropped it. It then hopped to the left, where it sat down. Here the print of the long tail can be seen, as well as those of the wings, and two little heaps of sand shovelled against the body by the wings. From here it has flown up, leaving two deep footprints when it did so

DO BIRDS LEARN BY EXPERIENCE ?

WE have seen that birds do many things which they can never have learnt to do, in this way being very different from humans, who have to learn so much. But to assume that birds cannot learn at all would be a mistake. In some respects their learning abilities are very good indeed. The field-watcher can sometimes observe striking instances.

A young bird does not have to be taught to fly; but when you follow the development of its flight performances in detail, you will see that the finer skill is acquired by practising, which, though it may have nothing to do with learning by imitation, is a kind of learning nevertheless. For most birds it is easier to fly up into the air than to descend and to alight. The first landing of a young bird may be a crash-landing. However, the second time they will land more carefully. Manœuvring in a strong wind is also a thing that improves with practice. Birds learn this in the way we learn to play a sport like soccer, or, more precisely, in the way we learn the technique of 'controlling' the ball.

A similar kind of learning may also be the function of the 'hunting games' played by, for instance, young kestrels. When young kestrels are fully fledged and already catch mice for themselves, they practise prey-catching in their 'spare time' for hours. Hovering in the air they select small objects on the ground, such as pine cones or tufts of grass, and then swoop down on them and 'catch' them. Hobbies play similar games, as I described on page 35, but their hunting games are performed in the air, and they use each other as 'prey'.

On the whole, however, the learning of new movements seems to be rare in the animal kingdom. Much more often birds learn to do inborn things in new circumstances. When a ringed plover, breeding on the bare shore, walks to the nest to sit and incubate (both inborn activities), the only thing that has to be learnt is where the nest is. That this is 'learnt' can be shown by a simple experiment. The nest, otherwise in bare sand, may happen to be near some object such as an old box. If we move the box a few yards, the bird, on returning to the nest, may go to the box, the landmark by which it has 'learnt' its way to the nest. Perhaps a week later, when it has got used to the box's new location and has re-learnt the way to the nest, we may move the box again, and again the bird will be confused.

We say that birds have learnt to recognize their young when they are willing to feed and brood them (themselves inborn activities), but not to feed or brood young of other pairs of the same species. This discrimination between young appears a few days after the young have hatched. If almost immediately after hatching you exchange young gulls of the same age but belonging to different nests, both parent pairs accept the change without demur. But if you do the same a week after hatching, they will not accept the foster-young but attack and kill them. It is perhaps better, therefore, not to repeat these experiments.

This type of learning—the confinement of certain activities to special individuals—is most pronounced in geese. When young geese hatch, they want to associate with their parents, but they do not know what their parents look like; they have to learn that. Goslings hatched in an incubator, when taken out and put on the ground, will follow their keeper as naturally hatched goslings follow their parents. After a few days with the keeper an attempt to bring them to foster-parents of their own kind causes them to flee from the geese and come after the keeper. Goslings learn what their parents look like in this short time, and because the keeper was the first living thing they saw after hatching, they 'learned' the wrong parent. In nature, of course, as the parents are the first creatures the nestlings see, this learning process never goes wrong.

A similar type of quick learning seems frequently to occur in the lives of song-birds preying on camouflaged insects. A bird appears to start searching for prey without knowing exactly what type it is looking for. Then, by accident, it finds a caterpillar—perhaps one that moved; and then it may concentrate on that species, finding more now that it knows what it is looking for. If it again stumbles upon another type, it may switch over to this new prey which it has learnt is also suitable food. In the same way the bird learns the appearance of those insects which are distasteful, and avoids them.

One other strange thing about birds' learning is that they use their considerable learning

Two fully fledged young kestrels practising a hunting game; the bird at the left has 'captured' a stick; the one to the right is just diving down on a pine cone

capacities only in special cases. Whereas herring gulls learn to distinguish their own young from all others, they rarely learn to know their own eggs, even when they are quite different from their neighbours' eggs. They learn to know their nest site and become so attached to it that if the eggs are moved a foot away but the nest left where it was, they will sit on the empty nest. But if the nest is destroyed, and they are offered the choice between their own clutch and a clutch of quite a different type, they will sit now on this and now on that clutch, apparently unable to make up their minds. Yet the eggs differ much more from each other than do the chicks that hatch from them. Somehow this difference in reaction to eggs and chicks has to do with the fact that it is sufficient to learn the location of the nest, for eggs do not walk away; but chicks do roam about and so have to be recognized if the parents are going to raise their own chicks. Why in such birds each pair should attempt to raise their own chicks is another question, which I will not try to answer here.

Man-raised goslings are not interested in mother goose

SOME
PRACTICAL
HINTS

LEARNING to know the ways of birds takes time, and requires visits to different localities as often as possible, at all times of the year. Here are some directives as to the methods a bird-watcher can apply.

Strong and warm field clothes of inconspicuous colours and stout shoes or boots are needed. Drab or khaki clothes are best. It is impossible really to get to know birds as a member of a crowd; it is better to go alone, or with one keen friend who can walk along silently without chatting, for it is important to be on the alert all the time. The early morning is the best time. Just an hour spent in the open before breakfast gives plenty of opportunity for seeing exciting things. Field-glasses are, of course, a great help, but they are not at all essential. By sitting down quietly on a not too exposed spot for an hour one often sees more than by walking for several

hours. Experience soon teaches one how to select a strategic observation post which gives a wide outlook as well as adequate cover. It is important to have the sun behind you so that the colours of the birds show up well.

At first you will often have difficulty in identifying the species, but if you mark the general appearance as well as specific details of your bird and note these down, you will probably be able to identify it from books at home. It is useful to make notes and sketches in the field; they are often a great help when back at home, and also these notes may grow into a journal which later may be very interesting.

It is useful to build hides at favourable observation posts. If you can select a shaded or partly covered spot at the edge of a copse, you can often, with very little trouble, add a screen of dead branches and bracken or reeds in front of it, in which you can make a good peep-hole. On the seashore it is often simplest to dig oneself in a little, and then build a hide with old baskets, boxes, and any suitable remnants that have been washed ashore. It is essential with all hides not only that the bird cannot recognize you through the front screen, but also that it cannot see your silhouette against holes in the back. I often hang my field jacket or oilskin behind me.

A hide on the Norfolk saltings during a spring tide, which washed the black-headed gulls' nests away

A hide made of an old basket, sacking, and sods

A little collapsible tent is useful. Anything can do as a hide so long as it is either camouflaged so that it does not show up in the surroundings or is made of something the birds are so used to that it does not disturb them. I once dug a hide in sand dunes, and covered it so well with sods and plants that I had the greatest trouble in finding it again myself! At another time I built a hide of bricks which had been piled up on a quay frequented by gulls. Though it was conspicuous enough, the gulls immediately came in front of the hide because the bricks had been there for weeks. I once took photographs of a sitting avocet in a flax-field on the isle of Texel simply by putting on the kind of blue jacket the local farmers wore and sitting down near the nest. During the week before, farmhands had been hoeing in the field and the bird had become quite used to them—but only to people in farmers' clothes, not to anyone else.

When at first I had tried to stalk the bird in my own field clothes, it had flown off long before I reached it.

Often it is possible to tame birds so that you can watch them without hiding yourself. Some people are especially gifted in this way, as you can see by reading Len Howard's *Birds as Individuals* (Collins).

Apart from stalking birds and building hides near their favoured localities, you can also attract birds to where you want them by, for example, putting up a feeding-tray near your home or providing a little pond where they can drink and bathe. If you can make the water move, for instance by letting the tap drip into it, it will be more conspicuous and so more attractive to them. In the nest-building season the provision of downy feathers or other nest materials soon attracts the birds; and to hang out an old stuffed owl, a cuckoo, a fox, or even

59

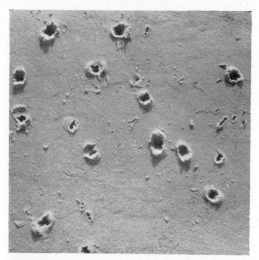

Where oystercatchers have been feeding on worms burrowing in the seashore. The narrow slits showing small lower mandible and large upper mandible indicate where the bird has merely probed; the large holes indicate deep borings

a piece of fur may bring about the most fascinating mobbing behaviour. But this should never be near the feeding-tray as it might scare the birds away.

Making collections of all kinds is interesting —birds' pluckings, owls' pellets, skulls and skeletons. Collections of photographs recording what has been seen are also invaluable. Many photographers concentrate on making pictures

of birds at the nest, but this is not a suitable thing to do unless you are very experienced, for it too easily disturbs the parent birds and endangers the brood. But there is still much to do on other phases of bird life, for example, photographing a woodpecker while opening up a pine cone which it has stuck into a slit in the bark of a tree, or a song thrush at work at its 'anvil', where it crushes snail shells. Migrants along the river's bank or male birds showing their threat displays near a stuffed owl or in front of a mirror make good subjects. Bird tracks are also an attractive subject, particularly such tracks as can show you something of what the bird has done. If you succeed in getting a good picture that at the same time tells a tale, you might even get your expenses back by sending it to an illustrated journal!

If you can draw at all, hardly anything can be as satisfactory as sketching. I have always derived great pleasure from making pencil or ink drawings while watching, and these are a valuable record. Without being in any way an artist you can, with a little practice, make something of great interest, and it is remarkable how many people can make reasonably satisfactory sketches. Drawing helps one to observe, for only when attempting to make a sketch do you realize aspects or parts of a bird which before had failed to catch your attention.

Opposite:

Some sketches from field notebooks, which are meant to demonstrate that even without being an artist one can add to the interest of field notes

1. *A female hobby robbing a male kestrel of its prey*
2. *A half-grown goshawk on the nest, showing a full crop after having been fed*
3. *Male snow bunting in spring, preening*
4. *Sketches of nestling hobbies*
5. *Black woodpecker working at its nest hole in a beech tree*
6. *Male snow bunting feeding on grass-seeds in spring*
7. *Red-necked phalarope making a scrape (above), swimming (centre), and attacking an intruder (below)*
8. *Male snow bunting showing off back pattern to female*
9. *Black woodpecker watching its mate above*
10. *Threat posture of male coot*
11. *Threat posture of kittiwake*
12. *Three sketches of song-flight of male snow bunting*

BIRD BOOKS, BIRD JOURNALS, BIRD CLUBS

THIS little book, though I hope it may convince you that watching the ways of birds is an interesting hobby, cannot help you to identify birds. There are several good books on bird recognition on the market. I can recommend to you Collins's *Pocket Guide Book to British Birds*, by P. S. R. Fitter and R. A. Richardson (21s.); James Fisher's *Bird Recognition* (Pelicans A 175, A 176, and two volumes still to appear; Penguin Books, 3s. 6d. each); and *A Field Guide to the Birds of Britain and Europe*, by R. Peterson, G. Mountfort, and P. A. D. Hollom (Collins, 25s.). The great standard work on British birds is the five-volume *Handbook of British Birds*, published by Messrs. Witherby, which can be consulted in many libraries. Volume II of the *Oxford Junior Encyclopaedia* also gives much useful background information.

Several books have appeared lately which demonstrate in much more detail than I can do here how much can be learnt by bird-watching, and how much even a beginner can contribute to scientific ornithology. Bruce Campbell's *Bird Watching for Beginners* (a Puffin Story Book, PS 71, 2s. 6d.) gives an excellent all-round introduction. David Lack's *The Life of the Robin* (a Pelican Book, A 266, 2s. 6d.) shows what can be done by the intensive study of one common bird.

Another way of keeping in touch with work being done is to take the monthly magazine *British Birds* (Witherby, 5 Warwick Court, London, W.C. 1; 25s. annually). For young people it is worth while to join the Royal Society for the Protection of Birds (82 Victoria St., London, S.W. 1), which organizes a Junior Bird Recorders' Club (ages: 11 to 18; subscription 2s. 6d.). At 17, you are entitled to join the British Trust for Ornithology (Secretary, Dr. Bruce Campbell, 2 King Edward St., Oxford) and to profit from their advice, field guides, &c., and to help them with their research projects, such as bird censuses. The Trust provides a list of bird clubs, and may be able to put you in touch with other bird-watchers in your neighbourhood. Even if you are not yet 17, you can ask for information, which they are glad to give.

Bird-ringing is a project which needs many recruits. But since the results of ringing have to be used as building stones for scientific work, the organizers are very careful to accept co-operation only from experienced ornithologists. Nevertheless anyone can take part in the work through the various bird observatories, where beginners can help and learn at the same time. Here is a list of bird observatories in Britain; those willing to join in the work can get more detailed information from the Trust:

Jersey Bird Observatory.

Lundy Field Station and Observatory, Ilfracombe, Devon.

The New Grounds, Slimbridge, Glos.

Stokholm Bird Observatory, Dale, Haverford-west, Pembs.

Cley Bird Observatory, Holt, Norfolk.

Gibraltar Point Bird Observatory and Field Study Centre, near Skegness, Lincs.

Spurn Bird Observatory, Kilnsea, Yorks.

Monk's House Bird Observatory and Field Centre, Seahouses, Northumberland.

Isle of May Bird Observatory and Field Station, Fife.

Fair Isle Bird Observatory, by Lerwick, Shetland.

A yearling grey heron fishing along a tidal creek. Its left leg bears a ring

ACKNOWLEDGEMENTS

THE ILLUSTRATIONS in this book are my own except the following, for which I am indebted to the colleagues mentioned: page 52 (P. Creutzberg); 12 top, 27, 41 (F. Kooymans); 21, 40 (J. Markham); 34 top (J. Strijbos); 24 top, 36, 37 top, 63 (L. Tinbergen).

The following illustrations are based on work of others, but were redrawn and simplified or amplified: 54 (J. Buxton); 11a, 22 (A. Daanje); 11b, 13 bottom (O. Heinroth); 25 bottom (D. Lack); 9 (K. Lorenz); 57 top (L. Tinbergen).

I am also much indebted to W. B. Alexander, M.A., for permission to reproduce Wolf's watercolour as a frontispiece.

PRINTED IN GREAT BRITAIN
AT THE UNIVERSITY PRESS, OXFORD
BY CHARLES BATEY, PRINTER TO THE UNIVERSITY